Her Debt Was Due—

Vidas stood watching her for a long moment, the keen deep-set eyes drinking in her beauty. Melanie blushed and turned her head. What had she done by agreeing to this?

'What are you thinking about?' he murmured as he pulled her close.

'I suppose I'm a little . . . scared,' she confessed.

His arms about her were masterful, his kiss demanding, yet tender. 'Are you still afraid?' he asked finally, his smile gently mocking.

Melanie shook her head as desire replaced every other emotion. "No, Vidas. I'm not afraid,' she whispered hoarsely. 'Kiss me . . . love me . . .'

ANNE HAMPSON
has the same impetuous streak as her heroines. It often lands her in the middle of a new country, a new adventure—and a new book. Her firsthand knowledge of her settings and her lively characters have combined to delight her readers throughout the world.

Dear Reader:

Silhouette has always tried to give you exactly what you want. When you asked for increased realism, deeper characterization and greater length, we brought you Silhouette Special Editions. When you asked for increased sensuality, we brought you Silhouette Desire. Now you ask for books with the length and depth of Special Editions, the sensuality of Desire, but with something else besides, something that no one else offers. Now we bring you SILHOUETTE INTIMATE MOMENTS, true romance novels, longer than the usual, with all the depth that length requires. More sensuous than the usual, with characters whose maturity matches that sensuality. Books with the ingredient no one else has tapped: excitement.

There is an electricity between two people in love that makes everything they do magic, larger than life—and this is what we bring you in SILHOUETTE INTIMATE MOMENTS. Look for them this May, wherever you buy books.

These books are for the woman who wants more than she has ever had before. These books are for you. As always, we look forward to your comments and suggestions. You can write to me at the address below:

Karen Solem
Editor-in-Chief
Silhouette Books
P.O. Box 769
New York, N.Y. 10019

ANNE HAMPSON
The Dawn is Golden

Silhouette *Romance*

Published by Silhouette Books New York

America's Publisher of Contemporary Romance

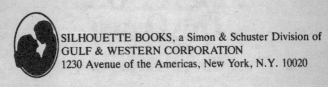

SILHOUETTE BOOKS, a Simon & Schuster Division of
GULF & WESTERN CORPORATION
1230 Avenue of the Americas, New York, N.Y. 10020

ISBN: 0-671-57220-2

First Silhouette Books printing May, 1983

10 9 8 7 6 5 4 3 2 1

Map by Ray Lundgren

America's Publisher of Contemporary Romance

Printed in the U.S.A.

Other Silhouette Books by Anne Hampson

GREECE

Places set in _italics_ are fictitious.

Chapter One

Melanie smiled at her sister and said how nice she looked.

'You've made a super job of that dress,' she added finally.

'Yes, I have to agree. Didn't know I was so clever with material and a sewing machine. Mind you, patterns these days are so simple that you'd be a duffer not to be able to produce something wearable.' Katie pirouetted before the mirror. She and Melanie were on one of their somewhat rare visits home for the week-end, enjoying the comforts of a country house and the company of their parents. For the most part they lived in a small flat in London convenient to their work, and it was only about three or four times a year that they came home, since the train fare up to the northwest was rather expensive.

'I do feel rather smug,' commented Katie as she began to comb her hair, pale gold hair that looked like silk. 'I might one day become a famous designer.'

Melanie laughed and brushed a hand through her honey-bronze hair, long and gleaming with health.

'Except that you didn't design that dress,' she was ready to remind her sister.

Katie said nothing and Melanie stood watching her adding the finishing touches—perfume and blusher. At the age of twenty-four, Katie was three years older than her adoptive sister and both worked in the offices of John Meyer Ltd., paper manufacturers.

Melanie's lovely grey-green eyes became more and more appreciative as Katie used the blusher. She was beautiful and no mistake, thought Melanie.

'Have a good time at the dance,' she said as she went from her sister's bedroom to her own, much smaller one. It was at the back of the house, while Katie's was at the front, facing the lovely meander of the river.

Standing by the window, Melanie was thoughtful. Cedric Granger was becoming rather serious and she could not quite decide whether or not she wanted the affair to progress beyond the stage it had already reached—that of good friends who enjoyed one another's company. Katie on the other hand was engaged to the eldest son of a millionaire, a handsome young man who adored her and whose parents had been delighted with the engagement. They were to be married in the autumn.

'Are you there, Melanie?' Her mother's voice

breaking into her thoughts. She turned to the door and called down,

'Yes, do you want me?'

'Your father and I would like a pot of tea, dear. This is a good play we're watching, so neither of us wants to leave it to make the tea.'

Melanie went down to the kitchen and laid the tray while the kettle was coming to the boil. She looked round, comparing the bright sink with the one in the flat, the polished teak cupboards with the dingy, painted ones to which she and Katie were used. When Katie left the flat would be hers, mused Melanie, and although it was only rented she felt she would try to afford the expense of making it a little brighter.

When she entered the living room her parents were sitting close together on the couch, holding hands.

'Ah, there you are! This is such a good play,' went on Mrs. Grayshott without moving her eyes from the screen. 'Why don't you watch it in the other room, dear?'

'I might go out.'

'Katie's been invited to a dance, she told me. How was it you weren't invited too?'

'Katie was out shopping this morning and bumped into someone she knew. They invited her to the dance. I expect they forgot to include me. In any case, I didn't bring a dress with me. Katie never comes up without a long dress, as you know.'

'Always the optimist.' Mrs. Grayshott's eyes were still firmly fixed on the screen.

'Lay our supper tray before you go out, won't

you?' interposed Mr. Grayshott. 'Biscuits and cheese and perhaps a scone. Er—where are you going?'

'There's a good film on at the Odeon.' She looked at him as he turned his head. He was greyer than she had noticed before and his pale blue eyes seemed tired. A tinge of blue about the lips was something she had not noticed the last time she and Katie were home. For some reason she was unable to explain Melanie had gained the impression that he had something on his mind. The idea came immediately she arrived home on Friday night and had persisted all today, Saturday. Somehow she was thinking about the fact that theirs was a highly respected family in the select neighbourhood of Transfield, their parents having some influential friends while the girls themselves were both admired for their attractiveness and charm of character.

But of course each was different. Mr. and Mrs. Grayshott had adopted Melanie when she was three months old, as a playmate for Katie who, the doctor said, would have to be Mrs. Grayshott's only child. Melanie had never asked about her parents but a snippet of conversation once overheard made her think she was the daughter of two young University students. She had no grumble; she'd been given a good home and education, and now she had an excellent post as secretary to Mr. Jenkins, under-manager of Meyer Ltd., while Katie was secretary to Mr. Meyer himself. Both girls were highly thought of in the firm and their respective bosses had complete trust in their honesty. It was nothing unusual when, the wages having arrived by van, the bag was handed by Mr. Meyer to one or other of the sisters to be put in the safe.

'I wouldn't bother about the film,' she heard her mother say as she straightened up after pouring the tea. 'This play is very interesting.'

'It's been started for over twenty minutes.'

Melanie went from the room feeling restless, unsettled. Was she just a tiny bit envious of her sister? It would not be surprising seeing that Hal was so nice, so charming to Melanie. He was just the kind of man she would like to have one day—handsome and tall, of a good family and with far more gallantry than was fashionable today.

Melanie recalled the day Hal had come into the office, his having an appointment with Mr. Jenkins. He had smiled and Melanie's heart seemed to turn a somersault. She had been chatting happily with him as he waited for Mr. Jenkins to come from his lunch. Then Katie had entered the office—Katie with her pale gold hair and ethereal appearance. She had seemed stunned for a moment, mesmerised by the man sitting there, chatting to her sister. It wasn't unusual for Katie to take over and very soon Melanie was excusing herself and leaving the two alone together.

The engagement was announced two months later. . . .

The two sisters stared at one another, their faces white.

'I can't believe that Father's been embezzling—' Katie with tears in her eyes was shaking her head. Melanie, equally bewildered, found herself so tight inside that she was unable to cry. Her stomach was in knots, her nerves stretched ready to snap. For their solid little world seemed about to topple.

'I can't, either, but he's admitted it.'

'When Mother gets to know she'll have a breakdown. She adores him.'

'It's a wonder he confided in you.'

Katie bit her lip.

'He was driven to it. If he doesn't find the money by next Friday he's to be prosecuted by his firm.'

'Is there nothing we can do?' Melanie's mouth trembled but she was still unable to cry.

'I've been searching my mind and can't think of any way to get a sum like that.'

Melanie shook her head slowly from side to side, murmuring to herself,

'Eight thousand pounds. . . .'

'Neither you nor I have anything like that saved up between us.' A pause and then, slowly and thoughtfully, 'I wonder if we could borrow it? Banks are eager at present to make loans.'

'Not without some form of security. It wouldn't make sense.' Melanie moved over to a chair and sat down. 'I have about a thousand in the bank. As you know, I've been saving hard for the cruise I'm taking in September.'

'I have about the same,' musingly from Katie. 'Mine was for my trousseau.' Her mouth quivered and the tears escaped.

'Was?' echoed her sister, puzzled.

'I can't see Hal wanting the daughter of a—a jail-bird—'

'Don't!' cried Melanie in a distressed voice. 'He isn't— I mean, it won't come to that.'

12

Katie's big blue eyes widened.

'It must,' she asserted. 'He's admitted being threatened. And you know what his boss is like. I never could take to that man; he seems so hard.'

Reluctantly Melanie nodded in agreement.

'I'd steal it if I could!' she declared vehemently. But of course she didn't mean it.

'So would I. However, that's an unprofitable idea,' Katie added finally.

The gloom was overpowering in a room that always had been friendly and warm, the main living-room of the smart detached house which boasted its acre of well-kept gardens. Yes, the Grayshotts were indeed among the elite of the community.

'Where is Father now?' Melanie inquired at last. She supposed it was natural that he should have confided in Katie first, seeing that she was his own daughter—not adopted like Melanie.

'Out there, in the greenhouse.'

'I feel . . . awkward.'

Katie shot her a glance.

'You're not thinking of going out to him, are you?'

'I feel he needs comfort.'

'He's certainly as low in spirit as can be.' A pause ensued before Katie added in disgust, 'Gambling! I'd never have believed he could do it. And as I said, all for a new car!'

'The one we have is super.'

'Of course it is, but nowadays this keeping up with the Joneses seems to have become an obsession with some people, and obviously Father is one. He's always envied the Faradays their cars and when the Mercedes arrived three months ago—' She spread her hands. 'That was it, apparently.'

'So trivial a reason for gambling.'

'And stealing to do it,' added Katie through compressed lips.

'Don't mention that word, please,' begged Melanie, and was told to be realistic and accept that their father was a thief.

'When is he going to tell Mother?' Melanie was wanting to know a moment later.

'I expect he'll hang on as long as he can. People do tend to put off disagreeable things when it would be best all round if they didn't.'

'But as you say, Mother will have a breakdown. She hasn't actually been in the pink of condition lately, you know that.'

'And Father . . .' Katie paused in thought, a deep frown marring her lovely face. 'You know, Melanie, I have a feeling his heart might be weak, and a trial and jail sentence could kill him.'

'No! Don't keep on seeing only the worst side!' protested Melanie and was again admonished.

'Face facts, for goodness' sake! This is a real situation even though it's one which normally happens to others and not to you! Father's about to be arrested, to face a trial, to be sentenced. You and I—and Mother—are going to feel the impact. Thank your lucky stars you aren't engaged to a man from a prestigious family as I am. I've everything to lose, whereas you have very little.'

Melanie said nothing. She wasn't thinking of herself and any disgrace that might reflect upon her; she was thinking of the man who had given her a home, and of his wife who had been a mother to her.

And she was thinking of Katie who was madly in love with a wonderful man. . . .

'Katie,' she sighed at length, 'is there no way out of this at all?'

'Not that I can see.' Flat the tone and the tears oozed from the big blue eyes. Melanie swallowed but the tightness in her throat remained. As did the knots in the pit of her stomach.

'I don't think I'd go out to Father,' advised Katie. 'At present he's not told anyone but me. You'll do more harm than good if you go to him.' Being Sunday, the girls were getting ready to leave.

Melanie nodded in agreement, yet she wanted to go and comfort her father because, blameworthy as he was, he had lived an impeccable life up till now, had been a good and loving husband and father.

'You can't condemn a person for one single slip,' she heard herself say, and Katie merely looked at her with hard eyes and turned away.

'Miss Grayshott, put this in the safe. I can't think why the wages have arrived three days early. Perhaps there's going to be a strike somewhere along the line.' Mr. Meyer shook his head, but there was a smile in his eyes as he looked at Melanie. 'Here are the keys. Bring them back immediately you've locked the money up.' He glanced at the clock. 'Sorry if you're to be delayed—'

'It's nothing, Mr. Meyer,' broke in Melanie, picking up the bag with one hand and accepting the safe key with the other. There was a combination lock as well, but both Melanie and Katie knew what it was. 'I'm not going anywhere this evening.'

He went out and Katie came in, passing him in the doorway. Her eyes flew to the case, strong leather and with a sturdy brass lock.

15

'The wages, already?'

'They've come early this week. Mr. Meyer suggested there might be a strike in the offing and that's the reason why they've been delivered early.' She was about to go into the next room when the phone rang and she put down the bag.

It was Cedric and he wanted her to attend a dinner party with him that very evening.

'It's short notice,' she frowned even while thinking she would rather enjoy an evening out. It would take her mind off the tragedy that was about to befall her family.

'I know and I'm sorry. But I wasn't going to go—felt I ought to be studying. However, Jim rang and said another couple had let them down and he begged me to reconsider—said I must get you to come along as well.'

'Okay,' agreed Melanie and glanced at her watch. 'What time did you say?'

'I'll pick you up at seven.'

A small sigh escaped her as she replaced the receiver on its hook. She explained and her sister was swift to say,

'Go off, then, Melanie. I'll see to the money.'

'Oh, will you?' eagerly. 'Thanks a lot, Katie. I'll run for our usual bus, then!'

The following morning Melanie expected her sister to ask about the dinner party and was surprised when she made no reference to it at all. She had been in bed when Melanie was brought back to the flat at well after midnight by Cedric, who saw her safely inside and the door securely closed.

'Are you all right?' On a more close scrutiny,

Melanie was frowning at the pallor of Katie's face, the tightness of her lips. She was toying with her food, too, as if she had her whole concentration on something else. She glanced up at Melanie's inquiry, but for a long moment she seemed unable to speak, and suddenly there was a thickness in the atmosphere, something indefinable but which, to her amazement, was bringing the fine hairs springing up on Melanie's forearms.

At last her sister spoke, the words having a sort of strangled sound, not at all the musical tone which was part of Katie's attraction.

'I phoned Father immediately I arrived home from the office yesterday.'

'You did,' frowned Melanie. 'I didn't hear you.'

'You were getting dressed to go out.'

Melanie looked inquiringly at her.

'Has Father told Mother yet?' She was staring at her sister, that feeling of unease increasing with each moment that passed.

A small pause and then, slowly and very quietly as Katie left her toast and leant right back in her chair,

'There wasn't any need—' She stopped, then continued with difficulty, 'I— I had the money to give him—last night—'

'You—!' Melanie put her coffee cup down with a little bang on the saucer. 'I don't understand. Where did you get it?'

Katie swallowed hard as if her throat were blocked.

'He came down right away in the car and I gave it to him—'

'Katie!' broke in her sister pressingly. 'I asked where you managed to get the money?'

Katie avoided her eyes as she said, still in the same slow and difficult manner,

'I took it from the wage bag. Father thinks I—'

'Took it from—!' Melanie shook her head vehemently. 'No, you wouldn't! I don't believe you! Katie, this is no time for jokes!'

Suddenly Katie's expression was belligerent.

'It isn't a joke. I had to save him—and Mother and myself! I cut a hole in the leather—and—and t-took eight th-thousand pounds.'

Silence, the deep hush of disbelief paradoxically mingling with acceptance. Katie would never invent a story like that. *No, it was true. . . .*

Every nerve in Melanie's body began to riot; she felt choked and seemed to be going hot and cold in a matter of seconds.

'You—you stole the firm's money,' she breathed, her face a ghastly yellow though she was unaware of it. Damp tendrils of hair were glued to her forehead and her heart was pounding wildly against her ribcage. 'You actually stole?'

'I admit now that it was on impulse and that if I'd stopped to think I might not have done it.' All the strength seemed to seep out of Katie's body and it sagged in the chair. 'The bag . . . and all that money. The office empty of people. You said you'd steal to save Father if you could and it was because your words kept ringing in my ears that I did it. I don't think I was quite sane at that moment. I had to save us all, but especially I was thinking of Hal and his parents and the result if Father was tried for theft. I love Hal so! I couldn't bear the thought of losing him, Melanie . . . !' Katie was sobbing into her hands and for a while there was nothing in the room but the terrible sound of it. Melanie felt drained, ill. 'I thought also of Mother, who would have had a stroke—or something, and Father m-might die in jail—' The words came in spasmodic bursts between sobs which racked Katie's slender body. As for Melanie—she was glued to her chair after trying vainly to get up and go to her sister. 'The knife you'd used to cut open that cardboard box,' continued Katie after a while, 'was there, on the desk—tempting me! I knew I could save us all and I did! So don't look at me like that, Melanie! Don't condemn me, please. It was partly your doing, with saying you'd steal—'

'Katie,' managed her sister at last, 'you must return the money. I don't know how we're to get the keys if we've no excuse to offer,' she added with a swift frown, 'but we must! And if you've cut the bag open—'

'You seem to forget that I've already given Father the money at eleven o'clock last night. He'll be paying it back this morning.'

'You'll have to phone him at once,' said Melanie with an urgent glance at the clock. 'Tell him the truth; he'll not want to keep it if you do. I guess he'll bring it down later this morning and if we're lucky we can return it.' She paused in frowning thought for a long moment and then added decisively, 'We'll have to tell Mr. Meyer exactly what happened—'

'That Father stole?'

Melanie nodded her head at once.

'Yes, everything, and that on impulse you took the eight thousand pounds.'

19

Katie was drying her eyes and when presently she looked at her sister her manner was again belligerent.

'I'm not upsetting Father at this stage,' was her determined rejoinder. 'He was so relieved, and thanked me profusely. He feels he'll be sure to get the sack but intends to see his doctor and get him to say he has to retire early owing to his health. Mother need never know anything about the embezzling.'

Melanie could only stare for fully thirty seconds.

'You've saved Father,' she said, 'but only temporarily. What about you—?' She broke off and looked swiftly at her. 'What explanation did you give for having an amount like that in your possession?'

'I was going to tell you when you interrupted me. I said I'd had a win on the Premium Bonds.'

Melanie's eyes opened very wide.

'Didn't he think it was a very strange coincidence?' she asked, and Katie gave a small shrug of her shoulders.

'He might have done, but he was far too relieved to begin asking questions. He sensibly took the money and went off—'

'The whole thing's ridiculous!' snapped Melanie. 'You don't suppose you are going to get away with the theft from the wage bag, do you?' To Melanie's surprise her sister bypassed that and with a glance at the clock said briskly,

'We'd better be moving if we don't want to be late for work.'

So calm, now that the bout of emotion was dissolved!

'I don't feel like going in.' For the life of her Melanie could not imagine how she could go into the office and act normally with a thing like this on her mind.

'We'll have to go in.'

'On Friday the bag will be taken out of the safe.'

'That's two days away. I'll think of something before then.' Katie shot her sister the most odd glance and again Melanie felt prickles of rising hair on her forearms.

'You can't think of anything and you know it!' Melanie shook her head. 'No, you can't. You'll have to own up—or be prosecuted, and if that happens— Oh, Katie,' she cried in deep distress, 'what made you do anything so foolish! It's going to be worse than before because two of you are now involved, since you'll have to confess that the money was for Father. Mother will never get over it—never!'

Katie seemed not to be affected by this outburst; she was staring at Melanie with that strange expression and then she said softly,

'I have an idea but . . . well, you are involved and you might not agree.'

'I'm involved? In what way could I possibly be? I didn't take the money.' For some reason Melanie felt a terrible sickness in the pit of her stomach. 'You'd best tell me now and get it over and done with.' She glanced at the clock and decided all at once that she was definitely not going into work today.

'I have been wondering if—if y-you would take the blame.'

Silence, the all-enveloping hush of sheer disbelief.

'Do you know what you're saying, Katie?' How she managed to speak at all was a marvel to Melanie, but greater still was her ability to sound normal. Her mouth was dry, her throat felt blocked.

'You actually want me to take the blame, to leave myself open to prosecution?'

Katie rose to her feet. She was distressed and her eyes were swollen, but there was something about her that was hard . . . and almost viciously persuasive as she said,

'If I go to jail it'll hurt our parents far more than if you do.'

Amazement widened Melanie's eyes to their fullest extent.

'Katie, you don't know what you're saying. You can't think straight—'

'I can, Melanie. It's you who haven't considered the situation. Mr. Meyer brought the money to you to put into the safe—'

'But you did the job and returned the keys to him!'

'Taking the keys back has nothing to do with what I'm trying to get straight in your mind.' Katie was showing signs of impatience now, having seemingly recovered fully from the emotional upset of such a short time ago.

'There is no explanation you can offer that will make me take the blame,' Melanie could not help inserting as her sister paused for a moment.

'Try to see the whole situation objectively,' said Katie with a sigh of annoyance. 'You haven't even thought about my suggestion! If I own up, as you want me to, the money will have to be returned— *from Father's boss,* just as you said a moment ago. And we could then *both* be jailed, Father and me; it would just about finish Mother, loving us both as she does, so deeply.'

'You're saying that she doesn't love me so much

and, therefore, it wouldn't hurt if I was the one to be in disgrace.' Bitterness and glacier cold Melanie's tone as these words left her lips.

Katie let that pass as she said,

'My parents have done much for you, Melanie, and now you have a chance to repay them. If you take the blame and disappear—'

'Disappear?' quivered Melanie, aware that she was chilled from head to foot. 'Where would you have me disappear to?'

'You have a thousand pounds. I'd let you have what I've saved to add to it. Go away to the other end of the country and lie low. It isn't as if we visit our parents very often, so they'll not miss you— Just listen!' added Katie with a heavy frown as her sister would have interrupted. 'You can write, as usual, once every three weeks or so as you always do, and send the letters on here for me to post. I'll post the answers to you.'

Melanie gasped at this cool planning, realising for the first time that there was another side to the character of the girl whom she had hitherto believed she knew so well.

'The police,' she began, when Katie broke in to say,

'I shall tell them we're orphans, which will mean they'll not start looking for parents. I shall be able to convince them, so don't worry. It's fortunate that our employers never take an interest in us other than our usefulness in the office. No one knows anything about our private lives because we've never talked much—and I suppose that's because Father and Mother live such a long way off.'

Again so calm! Melanie recalled that a few of their colleagues must know they had parents, but for the moment that was of no importance whatsoever.

'This disappearing trick,' she said, becoming curiously interested in what was still within her sister's scheming mind. 'Am I to fade into oblivion indefinitely?'

'I guess that wouldn't be possible,' was Katie's rather casual reply. 'But it would at least give us time to think something up.'

'How very simple!' retorted Melanie with heavy sarcasm. 'The police aren't so dumb as to take your word that we're orphans.'

A sigh of impatience was the only sound for a few seconds before Katie said,

'I know I can convince them. If you run off—supposedly with the money—they'll concentrate on finding you and be so busy with the task that they'll not bother about parents, or wonder if you have another home besides the flat.'

'It wouldn't work even if I agreed. . . .' She tailed off as an impatient sigh escaped her sister.

'We'd better be off to work,' she suggested. 'We'll talk again this evening.'

How Melanie managed to get through the day she would never know. Katie went off to work but Melanie told her to make an excuse. She, Melanie, wasn't well. Katie seemed rather more than satisfied by this and it only struck Melanie later that she was playing into her sister's hands by staying away from work, which was the scene of the crime!

Hal called that evening after the girls had eaten. Katie had just gone off to the late-opening supermarket for some toiletries and it was left to Melanie to talk to Hal until his fiancée came back. As always, he was charm itself to his future sister-in-law and tonight he said with a sudden frown,

'Are you all right, Melanie, dear? You look—well —upset about something.'

'I'm a bit tired, that's all. Are you and Katie going out this evening?'

He shook his head.

'No, I just called in as I was passing.' His eyes smiled. 'Can't resist seeing my lovely girl,' he added, and Melanie thought about the situation and the probability of the engagement being broken.

Melanie left him and Katie alone but he didn't stay long, and Melanie had the strong suspicion that Katie had made some excuse to get him to leave.

'Have you thought about it?' Katie said almost before he had closed the door.

'You will have to own up.'

Katie was by the window, staring out

'Mr. Meyer was still at the office when I left. He went to the safe.'

'He—d-did?' Melanie felt a choking sensation in her throat.

'He's bound to know by now that he's been robbed.'

'By you.'

'He won't believe that either of us would do a thing like that. However, he'll obviously have been in touch with the police. . . .' Her voice trickled away to a cracked little silence. When she turned from the window her face was ashen. 'There's a policeman in the square now. . . . He's coming here.'

'Are—are you sure?' Melanie began to tremble.

'You'll have to—to own up,' she faltered, her whole nervous system out of balance. 'You will, Katie, so—so you might as well try to figure out what you're going to say—'

'He's gone!' Katie had turned to the window again. 'I can just see the back of him disappearing round the corner of the far flats. He wasn't coming here after all.' She sank down into a chair, trembling visibly.

'This is awful—unbearable. I'm going to—to tell someone.'

'Who?' Katie looked directly at her and Melanie could find no answer.

'I can't think straight,' she complained. 'Katie—what on earth made you do it!'

'I told you, impulse and the desire to save everyone.'

'Everyone but me.' Melanie's voice was bitter.

'It's a case of three against one.'

'And you believe I shall allow myself to be the scapegoat?'

'I believe that when you have given it more thought you'll admit that the only solution is for you to take the blame and disappear.'

'I won't do it!' But even as she spoke Melanie realised she was experiencing a feeling of fatality, a sort of resignation with one part of her mind which was being fought by the rebellion of the other half. Katie persistently stressed the disasters liable to take place if both she and her father were to be arrested. Their mother would be alone in her distress. She had never been as close to Melanie as to her own daughter. This Melanie knew and had accepted.

'Father will be sure to have a heart attack,' went on Katie in her persevering way. 'He'll not survive in prison. Mother adores him—you very well know that people have always marvelled at the way they have stayed madly in love with one another. It would break them both and, added to all that, what about the disgrace? If you took the blame there wouldn't be any disgrace—'

'I've already told you, the police would look into my life, would go up and visit our parents and it would get into the papers. You can't keep a thing like that quiet even if I did decide to take the blame.'

Nothing was solved that evening but the following morning both girls were sent for and questioned by Mr. Meyer. Reasonably he pointed out that no one had had the key since it was returned to him. He spoke kindly, was bewildered and upset, and in the end he of course warned them that he was getting in touch with the police at once.

The ordeal of being questioned by the police was something Melanie would never forget as long as she lived. Katie, though, seemed to have acquired a cloak of protection and was staggeringly cool.

Melanie could not bring herself to say she had left Katie to put the bag into the safe, so she told a lie and said they were both there, and it was all right when the safe had been locked. Which one of them had actually locked the safe? Melanie said she couldn't remember but Katie stated quite firmly that it was Melanie who had locked it.

The police went away with no arrest being made.

'They intend to arrest us both,' stated Katie, and

Melanie felt sure this would be the case. And in court . . . Who was to accuse who? Could she, Melanie, denounce her sister? The girl whose parents had done so much for her? And what of Hal and the heartache he would suffer? Until now Melanie had determinedly refused to dwell on what his heartache would be.

'The police are here, in a car.' It was less than an hour after the girls had arrived at the flat that Melanie, unable to tear herself from the window, made the announcement. She had not eaten and Katie had merely picked. 'This time they really are coming to this flat.'

'Then for God's sake run!' Katie was desperate, while Melanie herself was beginning to experience a feeling of panic . . . and doom. 'Go, and think afterwards! At least if you've made a run for it they won't arrest me! Please, Melanie! You can go down the back stairs.'

Without waiting for Melanie to make up her mind, Katie went to the bedroom and grabbed a coat and Melanie's handbag.

'Take these for now,' she urged desperately, 'and get in touch with me by phone later tonight! No, tomorrow, as the phone might be tapped tonight! Next week might be best—! Oh, for pity's sake—go!' The coat was flung at Melanie, the bag pressed into her hand. Melanie's mind had become a complete blank; she was as a robot . . . being led, or a puppet . . . with someone pulling the strings. Dazed and yet with a subconscious awareness of urgency and desperation, she managed to move, and left the flat by the back stairway, the coat dragging behind her, the handbag clutched tightly between frenzied fingers.

It was only when, clear of the porch at the bottom of the stairs, she came to put on the coat, that she realised it was not hers at all, but Katie's.

And it was bright red. . . .

Chapter Two

When she left the flat it never dawned on Melanie that the police would have time to spot her before she could put some distance between herself and them. She felt sure that Katie would manage to keep them talking, but that was not the case. Melanie was hurrying from the square when the car started up and came towards her. She started to run, thankful for the dusk which meant that darkness would not be long. She managed to dodge into a narrow alley and emerge at the other end where she could mingle with theatre-goers and those hurrying home after working late. There were plenty of people . . . but she had on a bright red coat.

However, she did manage to hail a taxi and she slid in without even glancing back to see if the police car was in sight.

'Where to?' The taxi was already moving and Melanie stared stupidly at the driver's back. 'Where do you want?' he said again over his shoulder.

'The—er—Waterloo Station—quickly. I shall miss my train!'

'What time is your train?'

'Er . . .' She glanced at her watch and had difficulty in seeing the hands.

'Half past eight.'

'You have plenty of time—more than plenty.'

He dropped her off. She looked about her as she paid him, and breathed a deep sigh of relief. But tears were close, for she had no idea where she intended to go. She ought not to have run away in a panic like that, influenced by her sister's urgency and her own anxiety for those she loved. But there had been no time to think.

Once on the station she stared about her helplessly. Then she lifted her eyes to scan the train times and destinations. Haslemere stood out as if in huge block capitals. It was, in fact, just one of several stops made by the train going to Portsmouth.

With her ticket booked she then wondered about the place and if there was an hotel. And when she was eventually on the train she found herself opening her handbag to see how much money she had. And she found her travellers cheques. She had bought them early so as not to forget them. Her passport was there, too, in a pocket. She had taken it with her when she went for the cheques, forgetting that one no longer needed to produce one's passport in order to get the cheques.

Haslemere was reached after what seemed an

31

eternity and she alighted, never in her life having felt so lost and alone, so helpless and weighed down by a feeling of doom. She told herself she had run away for nothing, since she must inevitably be caught sooner or later.

The road was dark after the station was left well behind but, her situation being what it was, Melanie felt the darkness and loneliness of the road was preferable to lights where she might be spotted, for she had convinced herself that her description would have been circulated to all police by now. On and on she walked, down one lonely lane after another, her mind a blank. Vaguely she knew she wanted an hotel but at the back of her mind was a fear of venturing into one, just in case she was seen by a policeman.

Lights of cars bothered her and she stepped to one side each time one came along.

And then came one with the light on top! Police! Terror seizing her, she forced her body through the prickly hedge and raced across a field. The car screeched to a stop, and too late she told herself that it was probably her suspicious behaviour that had attracted attention to herself. She raced on, reaching another lane, and there in front of her was a long, tree-lined drive. She took it without thought, aware that the car had taken the road circling the field and was now travelling down it towards the drive. Had they seen her? She cursed the red coat which would show up so clearly.

She had covered some distance before a house loomed up through the dull grey aura of advanced dusk. Vaguely her mind registered that it was a Tudor mansion, a house of charm and character but, undaunted, and further spurred on by the ominous sound of crunching gravel as the police car swung into the drive, Melanie raced on, taking a short cut across a lawn and eventually mounting the steps. She felt like an animal at bay, her breath failing rapidly, her legs like jelly, her mind fogged but yet registering the fact that two lights only were on in this dark and lonely edifice.

As she hammered on the door the only thought thrusting itself forward into her mind was that she would gain nothing, for who would proffer instantaneous help to a woman being chased by the police?

As soon as the door opened she catapulted herself into the hall, crashing against a tall lithe body which seemed to be made of iron. Weak and gasping, she clung to a white silk shirt and looked up at its owner with scared, desperate eyes.

'Help me!' she cried in wild and broken tones. 'Oh, please don't l-let them t-take me! Just give me a ch-chance to—to explain—' A choking sob in her throat stopped the rest, but already a slightly foreign voice was demanding,

'What the devil do you think you're doing?' The hands that had come out to grip her arms and push her away were as hard as the body, and the face above hers was so dark and forbidding that Melanie was tempted to turn and surrender herself to the police.

'I'm asking for help. . . .' The cold fever of doubt brought her plea to a lingering, uncertain stop as once again she looked into that darkly forbidding face. His eyes, black pools of basalt, fixed hers as a predator fixes its prey. Her face went as white as

33

chalk in the dumb, terrified silence, and she was thinking of Scylla and Charybdis, those redoubtable monsters, twin perils of legend, feared by mariners passing through the Straits of Sicily because one or other would be almost bound to destroy them.

Which must she choose . . . ?

Words came without her own volition and she was pleading desperately again,

'Help me! I'm being chased—! Oh,' she faltered as the car lights flared on coming round a bend in the drive which Melanie, in her haste and panic, hadn't realised was there. It meant that the men in the car could not be sure she had come to the door of the house, since it could only be seen once the bend was negotiated.

The man jerked her unceremoniously to one side and closed the door with a soft little click.

'Take that coat off,' he ordered with that alien accent which even in her present desperate plight Melanie found attractive.

But the idea of taking off her coat was certainly *not* attractive!

'For wh-what reason?' she stammered nervously.

'For one thing, the colour offends my eye, but more important, I want to see what you're like.'

She swallowed. Why should he want to see her without her coat? 'I want to see what you're like. . . .' It sounded ominous, to say the least.

'I—it isn't necessary—'

'Take it off.' The command was spoken very quietly now, but with the kind of emphasis which should not be disobeyed. Melanie felt she ought to give herself up to the police . . . and yet . . . At

34

least she might be given some sort of a chance if she did manage to get help from this man. The web of indecision was drawing more tightly about her, but she found herself doing the foreigner's bidding when the grind of wheels on gravel told her that the car was coming to a halt.

'You had better be quick.' The warning was spoken in slow and casual tones, as if the man were half-inclined to hand her over to the police and be done with it.

She dropped the coat on to the floor and stood before him, colour drifting into the pallor of her cheeks as she saw without any doubt at all that he was now keenly interested in her body. The dark and piercing eyes travelled with a kind of sensuous arrogance from her face to her feet and then, more slowly, back again, to rest for what seemed an eternity on the delicate, virginal outline of her breasts seen through the fine material of her blouse.

Her colour heightened and she squirmed when, after a hint of amusement had curved his lips, he allowed his eyes to wander again, and this time she felt she were being stripped naked.

Footsteps were heard, and voices. The foreigner gestured towards a door close by.

'In there,' he said shortly and gave her a shove which was anything but gentle. The long lean hand moved, too, from the middle of her back to curves much lower, and she felt their sickening warmth even after she was in the room and the door was closed upon her. There was a breeze entering the blackness and she realised that not only was a window open, but that she was standing right in its line. The wall by the side of this window offered support and she moved over to press her trembling body against it.

She heard the quiet rap on the oaken panel and the front door being opened. Voices drifted to her through the window where lace curtains were fluttering.

'. . . in the grounds, sir. We'd like to take a look around.' The voice was gruff but amiable.

'What is she wanted for?' The foreign voice now, sharp with interest.

'Only for questioning. She was acting suspiciously —bolted as fast as her legs would go when she saw the Panda car. Obviously been doing something she shouldn't have.'

Melanie cursed herself for her mistake. If only she had acted naturally she would not now be in this mess.

She heard the door close at last and within seconds the man was in the room.

'You were wise to keep away from the window. I didn't know it was open.' Walking over, he closed it and fixed the catch. 'You'd best come into the other room.' His voice was curt, without a trace of emotion. 'This way.' She followed him, nerves tingling, out into the lighted hall again and then into a charming room off it, a room with a log fire burning in the grate, its cosy glow showering the luxurious but comfortable sofa and chairs, the paintings on the walls, the massive oak beams and the wainscotting. Two muted wall lights were the only other illumination. She noted the heavy velvet drapes effectively shielding everything from any curious eyes that might be outside, drapes that reached from floor to ceiling.

'Well?' said the man briefly, without asking her to sit down. Melanie was again subjected to an all-examining perusal of her body.

'I didn't . . .' Her voice trailed. She had been about to say she hadn't done anything, but a shrewd glance at that face convinced her that she would never be believed, and in consequence would be handed over to the men outside. It took her a few seconds to decide what to say. 'I'm wanted for stealing,' she began. 'I—'

'Stealing?' sharply. 'What did you steal?'

'Money.' Melanie gulped and averted her eyes. She never had been able to lie and now she felt hot all over. 'Eight thousand pounds.'

Apart from an almost inaudible whistle there was no reaction to her words. She glanced up to find his face was a mask, but the eyes swung idly over her figure and came, as before, to rest on her breasts.

'Go on,' he said presently in peremptory tones. 'You had better not leave anything out,' he added as a final word of warning.

'I did it to save my parents—my adoptive parents,' she went on hurriedly. 'My father had embezzled money from his firm and would have gone to—to prison.' Her eyes were wide and appealing . . . and honest. The long dark lashes spread delectable shadows onto her pallid cheeks and her soft mouth trembled. She saw the man's eyes slowly narrow and take on a most baffling expression . . . but sensuality was there too, deep within those dark pools of basalt. She was scared, really frightened, but managed to gather herself with an effort. 'I stole the money from the firm where I worked.'

He said nothing for a long moment and then, tersely,

'You'll need to explain more fully before I make up my mind.'

There was an unfathomable inflection in the alien voice and for some reason Melanie was convinced that his mind was already made up: that he was not going to hand her over to the police.

The knowledge ought to have brought relief to her knotted nerves, but she was highly suspicious of the man's motives. She had heard no sound in this lonely house other than those which she and this man had made, and the voices of the policemen, of course. She recalled seeing only two lighted windows; one was the hall and the other this room which they were now in. Of course, some rooms at the back might be lighted but, somehow, she felt sure that there was no one in except this man and herself. The police were outside, searching the grounds; she could still give herself up.

'I asked you to explain.' The brusque voice cut her musings and she looked up at him.

'Can I sit down?' she asked, feeling her legs would not support her much longer.

'Of course.' He gestured languidly and she sank into the deep armchair indicated. He remained standing, tall and lithe without a dram of excess weight on his athletic body.

'Begin at the very beginning,' he ordered, and despite her doubts and misgivings Melanie did as she was told. The only vital part she omitted was that her sister was the real culprit. She saw no necessity for telling him that. For he might just decide to hand Melanie over to the police but to tell them they were chasing the wrong girl.

'So that is the whole story?' The eyes were narrowed and searching as they fixed hers.

'Yes, it's the whole story,' she lied. And hurriedly she went on, in case he should suspect anything, 'I had to do it, because my adoptive parents had done so much for me. I've explained to you just how much suffering would have resulted if I hadn't stolen the money and given it to my father.'

'So your mother never knew he had embezzled from his firm?'

'No; she was spared that.'

'And this sister—she can now marry her millionaire?'

'It's his father who's the millionaire,' she corrected. 'Yes, Katie can now get married.'

'So everyone's happy except you?' He spoke tersely and Melanie found herself trying to analyse the undertones.

'It'll be worth it,' was all she could find to say, and his straight black brows went up a fraction.

'Even if you are sent to prison?'

Her throat felt dry suddenly, constricted.

'I—you—are you intending to help me?' she managed in a tremulous tone.

'I haven't made up my mind.' He paused. 'This Hal you mentioned—would he have thrown your sister over for something her father had done?' Derisive the tone and the sensuous lips were curved in a sneer of contempt.

'His family are county people,' she submitted.

'I cannot see what bearing that particular circumstance has on the situation. However, it's of no importance. The important thing is what am I to do with you—?' He broke off and Melanie's eyes dilated.

'The police—they're back!' she gasped.

'Don't move from where you are!' He went to the door and opened it, passed through, and a moment later she heard him opening the front door in answer to the rat-a-tat of the knocker which a moment previously had brought Melanie's heart leaping into her mouth.

Would he give her up? Forbidding as he was, she realised with something of a shock that she preferred to be in his power rather than be arrested and probably sent to prison. Besides, there was the question of what she had done with the money. If she were questioned in the way the police were often accused of questioning their suspects, Melanie knew for sure she would break down, and once she had admitted the truth, her father would be arrested and the whole thing would have been for nothing.

'There's not a sign of her, sir. It's so dark, though, and these grounds are rather thickly wooded in places.'

'She's probably on a bus to Guildford by now.'

'Well, we'll see she's picked up and questioned. That red coat is a real giveaway!' The man with the gruff voice laughed.

'Good luck with your search. Sorry I wasn't able to help.'

'She might just come here once she sees us
40

leave—if she's still in the grounds, that is. You'll give us a ring?'

'Of course.'

'This is the number.'

'Thank you. Good night.'

'Good night, sir. Lovely place you have here.'

The door closed. Melanie leant back in her chair and breathed deeply. Her eyes were closed when the man returned but she opened them to see him standing in the doorway, an odd expression on his face. She would have given anything to be able to read his thoughts, for she did wonder if he were planning something. In effect he was merely allowing his critical glance to examine her face even more fully than before. He noted the fine intellectual eyes, the small retroussé nose and the delicate lines and contours of her face. The wide generous mouth was finely-modelled, as was the chin, firm and yet entrancingly feminine. Pointed, it lent an elfin quality to a face that attracted him more than all the other women he had met and had affairs with in his life. Her figure was slender and well-proportioned, her legs shapely enough to hold his attention for long enough to make her blush.

For her part, Melanie was equally interested as, with at least a respite to look forward to, she let her attention focus on the man who was the most distinguished and yet the most formidable she had ever met. She took in with appreciation the finely-chiselled classical features which were reminiscent of statues of ancient Greek heroes she had seen in museums; she was not so sure she admired the widow's peak which sliced a deep V into the lined and almost hostile brow, nor even those eyes, so black and all-seeing, so unreadable and hard. His body had already made an impression on her: she thought it must be perfect—well over six feet in height—and she had already noticed, too, an active grace about his movements. The arrogance about his mouth seemed to be an inherent part of its sensuality, and the dominant line of the jaw gave evidence of a man used to giving orders and having them obeyed on the instant. He came into the room at last and she heard him say,

'If you were on the run what, on earth made you choose to wear a red coat?'

'That? It isn't mine.'

His brows shot up.

'Something else you—er—lifted, eh?' He wagged a warning finger at her and gave her no time to speak as he added, his eyes slowly narrowing, 'Don't indulge in any light-fingered exercises here, my girl, or you'll answer to me. This doesn't happen to be my house.'

She had gradually coloured up as he proceeded, but anger was rising too, so that there was a distinct gleam in her eyes as she said,

'The coat belongs to my sister. She thrust it at me when we saw the police coming. As for my wanting to steal anything here—I'd be crazy to do such a thing even if I were—light-fingered as you describe me!'

'Be very careful,' he recommended in a very quiet tone. 'It doesn't say that because I've sent those men away that I've made up my mind to help you. Your exit from here could be just as dramatic as your entrance. I might just decide to take you by the scruff of the neck and throw you out.' The voice was still quiet, the eyes now idly flickering over her. She watched him lift a slender brown hand to smother a yawn. He said casually, 'Have you eaten?'

She shook her head.

'No, I haven't.' She had no appetite but felt it to be irrelevant to say so.

'Then we shall eat together and discuss what must be done with you.' Again Melanie would dearly have liked to fathom the undertones. 'I'm afraid you will have to help me prepare something. I was intending to go out and find a restaurant, but obviously you mustn't venture out just now.' He went on to explain that some mistake had been made in dates as to his visit to the friends who owned this house. 'Seems to have been Hilary's fault—she's the wife of Stephen, and a featherbrain, but charming,' he thought to add. 'I had business in London and said I'd come on here when it was finished and spend three or four days with them if it was all right. Hilary wrote back to say yes, but on my arrival this morning I was met by the daily help who told me that her employers were away on holiday in Italy.' He stopped and shrugged and seemed annoyed with himself that he could not be more brief. 'I decided to stay for one night and return to Greece tomorrow.'

'The daily help has gone home?'

'Of course.'

'So . . .' Melanie passed her tongue over lips that had gone dry. 'We're here . . . alone?'

'Quite alone,' with a sort of dry humour. 'Are you afraid?'

She swallowed hard, then shook her head—somewhat weakly.

'No, no—I'm not afraid. Why should I be?'

He laughed.

'Looking at you, I'd say you are the kind of girl who would be afraid. However, you seem quite sure that you are not, so we'll leave it at that.'

She shot him a glance, sure he was plotting something.

'I could leave—I mean—'

'So you *don't* like the idea of being here alone with me?'

'I'm not wildly excited about it.' This was out before she knew just what she was saying. It behooved her not to say anything this man might take exception to, for she was sure he could be dangerous. She need not have worried, for he gave another light laugh.

'Well, unless you intend to risk going forth again you'll be staying here all night.'

She ignored that with the kind of naive philosophy of a child: *leave it alone and it will go away!*

She said interestedly,

'So you are Greek?'

He inclined his head.

'The name's Vidas Loudaros. And yours?'

'Melanie Grayshott.' She paused a moment and then, 'Your home is in Greece?'

'I live on the island of Thristos.' The abruptness of this sentence gave the sign that he would not accept further questioning. In any case, he spoke before Melanie had time to do so. 'If you want to tidy up after that chase you've just had, there's a cloakroom to the left of the front door. Bend down as you pass the window; those guys might have come back to prowl around again.'

'Yes.' She looked up and managed a wan smile. 'Thank you for not turning me over to them.'

A lean brown hand was raised even before she had finished.

'Don't thank me yet. You might come to wish I *had* turned you over to them.' He looked straightly at her. 'I rarely do anything for nothing . . . and never for complete strangers.'

Melanie had begun to move to the door after taking up her handbag in preparation to go to the cloakroom. The move had brought her close to the Greek and now she halted abruptly at his words. She felt ripples along her spine; the very air seemed to prickle. The silence was broken by the chimes of a clock in the hall; to Melanie it was like a jarring siren as one thought whirred in her head: this man was a rake and an opportunist. She knew it even before she heard him say, as the hard eyes looked down into hers,

'You know, I had resigned myself to a dull evening alone. . . .' Mingling with the amusement in his voice was a trace of mocking satire as he continued slowly, as if to allow every word to sink in and be fully understood, 'But fate has sent me a very beautiful and desirable companion. We shall do very well together. Go and see to your face, then join me in the kitchen. You'll find it at the far end of the hall—' He gestured. 'This end.'

She could not move and for a space she could not speak either for her mouth and throat felt rough and dry. What had she landed herself in for? Why, she wondered bitterly, had she been drawn to this particular house, where an amorous Greek was alone . . . and, apparently, ready to take full advantage of what an obliging fate had thrown in his path?

'Something troubling you?' The smooth inquiry was accompanied by a glimmer of amusement in the basalt eyes. 'You appear to be undecided?'

She nodded slowly and mechanically, conscious of a wildly-beating heart and the terrified racing of her pulses.

She said through the roughness of her throat,

'I th-think I prefer to—to leave this house—if—if you don't mind?' Nervously she was gripping the handle of her bag, and she was aware of little beads of perspiration oozing from her temples. 'It is b-best that I g-give myself up.' Would he let her go? she wondered fearfully as she tried to see what was within the depths of those dark, immobile eyes.

'You prefer to leave?' His brows were raised a fraction. 'Prefer to spend the night in jail rather than here, in a comfortable bed?'

That he was deriving amusement at her expense was plain; if he thought to scare her further by the mention of the bed, he failed. She couldn't be more frightened than she already was.

'I want to leave!' A hint of hysteria echoed through the words as her voice tightened. 'Please let me leave this house—!'

'Don't panic,' he broke in with some asperity. 'If there's anything I detest it's an hysterical woman. Go and do what you have to do in there and then come to the kitchen. From what I saw when I

46

opened the fridge a short while ago it appears to be well-stocked with all we shall need.' He swung a hand imperiously. 'Off you go, and get it into that head of yours that you could be behind bars at this very moment if it weren't for my generosity in shielding you.'

Shielding her! From the police, yes . . . but what about the mischief he now had in mind?

But she moved, albeit slowly, and with almost laboured motions, and as she came abreast of him his hand came forth and her wrist was taken in a firm but painless grasp. She gave a cry and tried to twist away. Her strength was puny and she was brought with a jerk against a chest as hard as granite. And before she quite knew it her head was tilted by an arrogant hand and she felt the hot pressure of his mouth possessing hers in a moist and sensual kiss that seemed to last for an eternity.

At length he held her from him, and the expression in his eyes sent her heart lurching right up into her throat.

'What a find. . . .' His voice was faintly hoarse, his lips hard and demanding as they covered hers again. She felt his tongue and shuddered, then by force she was compelled to open her mouth and his tongue entered, sensuously caressing hers in the dark hollow where the skin was soft and pliable as gossamer silk. She ceased her struggles but fought for breath, squirming at the exploration of his hands, one of which had found her breast while the other was inside the waistband of her skirt, pressing her slender body hard against him to make her aware of his virility. Wild thoughts swirled about in her mind;

she had read about girls finding themselves in situations of danger like this, but never had she expected anything so frightening to happen to her. Would he take what he wanted and then murder her? Perhaps he would bury her in the garden and no one would ever know what had happened to her. Katie . . . her parents . . . Hal, dear Hal . . . Cedric . . . people passing into her consciousness and out again and all the while this amorous Greek trying to bring her to the point of willing reciprocation. And in fact Melanie did begin to know a fierce longing in her loins and her brain began to reel. A fleeting release of her lips afforded her the opportunity to cry out, to threaten, to assume an attitude of fierce rebellion and disgust. A low laugh convinced her of the futility of her efforts, and she wept as his mouth closed over hers again, moistly exploring, ruthlessly crushing the tender softness of hers. Then he was seeking the hollow of her throat and the vulnerable places behind her ears. She fought the primordial instinct to arch her body, to put her arms about his neck, to reciprocate to his kisses . . . and to enjoy the finesse of experienced hands and fingers seeking and finding all the hypersensitive places which she herself was only now realising she possessed.

He held her away at last, fully at arm's length, and his eyes seemed to glow like freshly-fanned ashes that had long been smouldering.

'A meal first,' he said thickly, 'and then . . .'

'No! Let me go!' She ran to the door and was pulled back by a tug of her hair. 'I don't want—'

'You will,' he assured her smoothly. 'Life is for living, girl! And you've just escaped a night in jail. I

can guarantee you'll be far more comfortable
... and happy, on a bed in this house than on a hard and
narrow pallet in a cold, white-walled cell.' He gave
her a shove with a hand on her backside. 'Go and
tidy that hair, and do the rest. I like my women to
look decorative when they face me at a table.'

Chapter Three

If Melanie thought to make her escape she was to be disappointed. For when she tried the front door, after watching Vidas move with that especial masculine grace to the far end of the hall and then disappear through a door, it was locked and the key had been removed. He had done that when the police had left! So he had the mischief in mind even then!

'What a fool I am!' she cried as she went into the cloakroom. 'I've asked for it! I guessed he was no good and so I should have run out and given myself up!' But even as these thoughts were whirling about in her mind they were being effaced by others. If she *had* given herself up the whole situation would have reverted back to square one. The whole truth would have been bound to come out. Katie's life ruined, and her parents'. . . . No, she, Melanie, must continue to be the one to make the sacrifices, and she could only hope and pray that the Greek would not murder her after the rape he was contemplating with such relish and satisfaction. The future . . . ? What would happen tomorrow when he left for Greece . . . ? These questions and numerous others were cast aside as she concentrated on washing her face and hands, then using a little make-up—just to give her confidence. She was still in the dark blue skirt and thin white blouse she had worn that day at work—was it only a few hours ago that she had left the office! A lifetime of fear and panic had been lived through since then!

When she had finished she stared at herself through the long, gilt-framed mirror. If only she had been ugly, undesirable to the beast! But her face, despite its pallor, was attractive. Her eyes, despite their anxiety, were appealing, with those long curling lashes framing them. Her hair shone like burnished bronze laced with pale honey and a few threads of pure gold. . . . A sigh escaped her as her eyes moved to examine her slender figure and to take in the tiny waist and the firm youthful lobes of her breasts, with the shape of the nipples clearly visible through the thin material of the blouse and the even less adequate lace of her bra. She lifted her eyes to the gentle slope of her shoulders, then to the curve of her throat.

She had always expected to keep herself for the man she would marry . . . but now . . .

Tears of self-pity were still in her eyes when she reached the kitchen. She put down her handbag on a chair and moved to where a bag of frozen sprouts had been placed on the draining board by the gleaming stainless steel sink.

'Shall I put these in a pan?' Marvelling at the calm clarity of her voice, Melanie picked up the bag and opened it. Vidas was by the cooker and she realised he had some steaks under the grill.

'Yes,' he said over his shoulder, and she was marvelling even more at the total absence of any emotion either in his voice or his manner. The scene of a short while ago might never have been enacted. And the man himself. . . . As he turned to look at her he might almost have been a celibate for all the interest he showed in her! Perhaps after all she *was* safe. Confidence rising within her brought a smile to her lips.

'Shall I use them all?' she asked, and he nodded his head.

'There didn't appear to be too many. Are you hungry?'

'A little.' She glanced at the china clock on the wall and saw that it was almost nine o'clock. 'I wonder what they are all thinking. . . .' She sent Vidas a startled glance for she had not intended to say anything like that. He was staring at her with an odd expression. 'It just came out,' she explained rather lamely. 'Thoughts put into words.'

He turned back to the stove; she watched him draw out the grill pan and stick a fork into the sizzling steaks. Quickly she poured hot water from the kettle on to the sprouts and took the pan over to the hotplate which he had already switched on for her.

'Do we need any other vegetables?' She backed away from him as he turned.

'Carrots, maybe. See if there are any in the freezer.'

She looked and found some which she soon had on another ring.

What a strange situation, she mused. She knew a feeling of unreality but her mind was vigilant. She felt there might just be a remote possibility of escape in some form if the Greek should become dangerous again. His threat was overt enough when he suggested they have 'a meal first. . . .'

The dining-room was cosy and inviting with its gleaming patinas on wainscotting, on a Jacobean chest and high-backed chairs bearing the carved initials M.S., obviously the original owners of the chairs and, perhaps, the lovely old oak refectory table.

Melanie laid two places opposite one another, then switched on the log-effect fire which stood in the lovely Adam fireplace. She looked at a silver candelabra which stood gleaming on the sideboard. . . .

'Light the candles.' A voice behind her brought her body swinging round. 'Might as well have a romantic setting—' He bent swiftly and kissed her full on the mouth. 'The vegetables are ready for straining—'

'I don't want a romantic setting!' flared Melanie, backing away from him. 'You're a stranger to me!'

'But a friend,' was his quietly spoken reminder. 'I've saved you from imprisonment—' He looked down at her admonishingly. 'Is this all the gratitude I get?'

'You didn't tell me what you wanted in return for your help!' she cried, aware that she was clenching her hands so hard that her flesh was hurting. 'If I'd known I'd not have hesitated to give myself up!'

'Liar. There was too much against it.'

She knew this was true. And, strangely, his calm way of delivering this truth quelled her wrath. Her lashes fluttered down; she had no desire to let him see that she agreed with him. But he was shrewd, and she heard him laugh.

'Light the candles,' he ordered again, and lifted her face to make her look at him. The eyes seemed to glitter and her previous tinge of optimism died. For a fiendish expression was what she saw, that of a ruthless womaniser, a man of opportunity. There was not one grain of pity in him, she realised. Fate had sent him a woman at a time when, disappointed at the absence of his friends, he had fully expected to spend a dull evening alone.

He would certainly accept what had so conveniently been provided.

All through dinner her mind echoed what he had said about there being too much against her surrendering herself to the police. But there was the other alternative: if she could escape and disappear without the police ever catching up with her— Melanie cut these thoughts. She would never be able to remain a fugitive for the rest of her life.

Sitting opposite to her, and leaning back in his chair with an empty plate in front of him, Vidas asked her what she was thinking about and she found herself telling him.

'It's all rubbish,' he stated, and she had to nod her head in agreement.

'I know.'

'Besides, I have no intention of letting you go tonight.'

She said in a tightened voice,

'I know that, too.'

'So you're resigned? I can't say if I'm glad or not. A fight is always rather entertaining . . . especially when I'm so sure of victory.' He paused, and then, his eyes never leaving her face, 'You're more desirable than ever when you blush like that. Am I right in thinking the experience will be new to you?' Amusement edged his voice but he seemed keenly interested in her reply.

'You are,' she said chokingly.

'Well, well, and how old are you?'

'Twenty-one.' She had a small amount of steak on her plate but suddenly she couldn't eat it.

'That's quite something,' he said, and leant forward to reach for the coffee pot.

'What is something?' She looked questioningly at him.

'A girl reaching the age of twenty-one and remaining a virgin in these enlightened times.'

She caught the danger that edged through the overtones of pleasantry. He was actually visualising the rape!

She heard herself say,

'You're heartless. I was most unfortunate to come to this particular house.' Somehow, bitterness seemed to calm her nerves and she leant back and relaxed.

'It's far too late now to have regrets or qualms about the wisdom of enlisting my help. As a matter of fact,' he added thoughtfully, 'you were better to come here than anywhere else because no one would have shielded you as I did.'

'How right you are.' She sent him a look of scorn. 'No other person would have had in mind the mischief that instantly came to yours.' She paused, amazed by her temerity when she found herself adding, 'Tell me about yourself, and your nefarious career as a rapist.'

She was not altogether surprised when he threw back his head and laughed, and yet, paradoxically, she had half feared some rather ruthless reprisal.

'You have a sense of humour in spite of your fears. Well,' he sighed, 'where to begin is the problem.'

'At the beginning, obviously.' She watched him pour the coffee and put the pot down again.

'I do not think you would be interested.' He spoke after an interval of thought during which his brow knit in a frown as if something cropping up from the recesses of his mind displeased him.

Or could it be that, for some incomprehensible reason, he did not want her to know about the more reprehensible side of his life? The idea staggered her but yet persisted. And his next words did much to strengthen it. 'Your innocent mind might be shocked—' He paused and smiled at her across the table. 'And we don't want that, do we?'

She said nothing, and the silence stretched. But it was by no means strained. Melanie was bewilderedly conscious of some emotion that was new, an emotion affecting her pulses and her heart even, for its beating had increased. She looked up, quite unaware

56

of fluttering lashes that sent adorable shadows on to her cheeks, of the effect of candleglow on her hair, turning it to a glorious russet-gold, of the man's keen interest in these things, or that he was finding a subtle perfection in the delicate lines of her face. His eyes were fixed and she thought there was a piratical look about them. The clock chimed the hour . . . ten. . . . She averted her head, and her spirits were dropping rapidly.

She said at last, forced to break the silence,

'After tonight? You'll be—be leaving, you s-said?'

'It's been troubling you?'

'I've been trying to put it out of my mind.' She threw him a wan sort of look. 'There were other things. . . .'

His lip curved slowly in the kind of smile she hated.

'The coming ordeal?' He shook his head. 'It'll not be that, I can assure you.' He paused while he took a drink of his coffee. 'I too have been thinking about tomorrow, and about your future. I have an idea— the only idea that can solve your problem. You'll come back to Greece with me.' He paused and a heavy frown knit his brow. 'Your passport,' he almost snapped. 'I'd let that slip my mind. Can you contact your sister and ask her to get it for you?'

'As a matter of fact I do have it—' She stopped. What on earth was she thinking about to be considering the man's proposal!

'You have?' in some surprise. 'Well, that's fine. I hadn't expected things to be simplified like this.'

'I can't go abroad,' she protested, her immediate danger totally forgotten for the time being. 'It's crazy!'

57

'On the contrary,' he argued calmly, 'it's the most sensible course you can take under the circumstances. You need to leave the country.'

She shook her head, but feebly.

'The future— Oh, there isn't anything for it but for me to give myself up!'

Her companion gave a swift exclamation of impatience.

'You've been into all that,' he admonished. 'Try to think straight—'

'Straight!' She glared at him. 'How can anyone in my position think straight?'

'You can at least try, instead of becoming hysterical at every turn.' So calm! Melanie could have hit him . . . had she dared. 'The future can take care of itself,' he continued in that same unruffled way. 'What should be concerning you at this moment is now—' He stopped and gave a low laugh. 'All right, tomorrow, then, seeing that now—meaning tonight —is settled. Tomorrow we'll go by taxi to London where you can do some shopping—get yourself a suitcase and some clothes to put in it. I'll phone the airport first thing to see if we can get seats on a plane. I expect it'll not be difficult. However, if not we'll stay at a London hotel for the night—'

'You seem to have it all planned to the last detail,' Melanie could not help inserting with a hint of sarcasm.

'I always try to be logical and to arrange things as simply as possible,' he agreed, deliberately bypassing the sneer in her voice. 'As I've said, I guess we shall get a flight to Athens tomorrow sometime, and from there we go by yacht to Thristos—'

'Yacht?' interposed Melanie with interest.

He inclined his head.

'I own a yacht,' he said simply. 'It's moored at present in Piraeus.'

She looked at him, at the jacket he had put on over the shirt which she had so unthinkingly clutched when she first shot herself into the house. It was of the finest linen and beautifully cut—expensive and in perfect taste.

'You're . . . rich?' She had no idea why she asked that but she found herself hoping he would not take it the wrong way.

He nodded casually and said,

'No credit to me; my father left me—comfortable.'

She frowned, admitting that despite the pagan aspect of his features there was, for all that, a subtle perfection in their sculptured lines. What a pity that such a man used his money in lustful pursuits instead of living a respectable life. She heard herself say as the thought occurred to her,

'You aren't married, or have children—' She stopped abruptly but too late. He was looking at her through eyes glimmering with amusement.

'I'm not married, but as for children . . . I hope not, but one never can tell.'

She blushed and his attention was again caught. He frowned a little and once again she felt he was not pleased with his private thoughts.

Did he wish he hadn't been such a rake? If so, why?

'You were talking about your yacht.' She mentioned that merely for something to say.

'It will take us to my island—'

'Your island,' she broke in wonderingly. 'Do you *own* an island!'

'I own about three-quarters of one.' His mouth tightened all at once. 'Someone else owns the rest.'

'You would like to own all of it?' The question came unbidden, result of something that was apparent.

'I *shall* own all of it,' he gritted, and she gave a start at the rapid change in his features. Harsh lines and a tightened jaw, dark embers of wrath within the depth of his eyes. He sipped his coffee slowly, his brow furrowed in thought. But soon he had thrown off whatever had troubled him and he was saying coolly, 'I have a large enough villa for you to share it—'

'I have no wish to share your villa!'

He glowered at her from above the rim of his coffee cup.

'Will you stop interrupting, girl! If you refuse to fall in with my plan you'll be a fool!'

She bit her lip, knowing he was right.

'You're suggesting that I—I—er—be your—mistress—permanently?'

'You have the idea,' was his matter-of-fact rejoinder. 'Stop looking so gloomy about it,' he went on in a softer tone of voice. 'I assure you you'll not be disappointed. I usually please those whom I favour with my protection.'

'Favour!' she ejaculated. 'What an opinion you have of yourself! I want none of your favours, thank you!'

He gave a deep prolonged sigh of asperity.

'It would seem, then, that you do intend to give yourself up tomorrow morning.'

Tomorrow morning . . . he wasn't even thinking of allowing her to give herself up tonight.

'I can't think!' she protested, and to her disgust her eyes filled with tears.

'If you do surrender to the police you'll have your mother go into a decline and your father die a lonely death in jail, to say nothing of Katie's broken heart—'

'Shut up, will you!'

'Let us get back to a commonsense attitude to the problem. As I said, you'll not be disappointed. And you'll have a rather pleasant life on the whole. I shall put a car at your disposal, and as for such things as chores—you'll never need to soil those pretty hands of yours again.'

'Again?' she echoed, desperately trying to rid herself of the draw of his attraction. Subconsciously she had been affected by it almost from the first, from the moment when she had let her hands come into contact with his body. And a short while ago when he had kissed and caressed her. . . . No use denying that something had been awakened within her that she had never experienced before. Now, as she looked at him and again admired the superlative structure of his face, she knew tinglings of something that was pleasant when in reality she ought to have been able to look upon that face with repugnance. 'What happens when you tire of me? After all, it would seem that you tire very quickly, seeing that you've had dozens and dozens of women.'

The basalt eyes opened very wide indeed, and the

firm line of the mouth relaxed in a smile of sheer amusement.

'Dozens and dozens?' he echoed. 'My dear girl, what gave you that idea? I'm no superman,' he added with a laugh.

Colour flooded her cheeks.

'I suppose I had formed a picture of hun— I mean, a great many women.'

Vidas pointedly changed the subject, asking Melanie if she was in favour of the plans he had made. She looked at him with amazement. So calm! So sure that she was meekly to go like a lamb to the slaughter.

And yet, what other course was open to her?

'I'll make up my mind in the morning,' she told him unthinkingly.

'You want to have a tryout first? Is that it?' He was laughing at her with his eyes and even more colour surged into her face.

'No such thing!' she flung at him. 'I was only thinking that it's a decision I can't make in a hurry.'

'On the contrary, it's a decision that you can't hesitate about. Tonight or tomorrow—' He flung a hand expressively. 'The answer will have to be the same.'

The tears that had come to her eyes fell slowly on to her cheeks. Vidas watched her with what to Melanie was almost callous indifference. He had no heart, no sensibilities, no compassion. He had not given her any answer as to what would happen to her once he tired of her, and she knew for sure that he would tell her to leave his home and not care a rap for her future. Yet she was seriously considering his proposal, simply because it did solve her own problem and made everything right for her parents and Katie. Yes, his proposal *had* to be accepted, she was soon telling herself, and the tears fell more freely down her cheeks.

'I think we'll have a cognac,' she heard him say in a brusque voice. 'You go and make some more coffee while I pour it.'

She lifted a surprised face and stared at him for a moment without speaking. His mouth was tight and yet the ruthlessness seemed absent.

'I don't want any—any brandy,' she said in husky tones.

'It'll do you good.' Imperious now his manner as he rose from the table. 'There really isn't any need for all this misery,' he said in passing. 'You ought to be counting the advantages instead of wallowing in self-pity.' And without affording her the chance to release the angry indignation she felt he had left the room.

She went to the kitchen, glancing up the wide, balustraded staircase as she did so. It was a beautiful house and she wondered what the owners were like. She felt that someone very nice would live here and wondered how they came to have friends like Vidas Loudaros.

She made the coffee and Vidas was standing by the table when she carried it in.

'Perhaps we'll take it to the other room,' he suggested, and took the tray from her. She followed, vitally aware of him as a man, profoundly conscious of being alone with him and completely at his mercy.

She had dried her eyes but had noticed in a mirror that her pallor had intensified to the white of alabaster.

Vidas flicked a hand, indicating a low, well-cushioned armchair, and she sank into it. She was tired and dispirited and felt the oppression of impending doom heavy within her.

'Here, drink this.' The glass he gave her was half full and she shied away from it.

'There's far too much,' she objected. 'I don't normally drink.'

'Take it,' he commanded and she obeyed, crushing the rebellion mounting inside her. If only she could retaliate, conjure up the courage to throw the glass and its contents at him!

Instead, under his watchful eye, she sipped it and to her surprise the warm feeling it spread over her was far from unpleasant. She took some coffee, vitally alert to the fact that she must not let the brandy affect her thinking.

It was about half an hour later that he said,

'We'll go up now that you've finished.' It had taken her long enough, he seemed to add as he glanced at her glass and cup, set on a small table at her elbow. 'I daresay we can fit you out with anything you need. . . .' He paused, and his sensuous eyes swept over her from head to foot. 'Perhaps you are one of those who prefer a nightgown.'

The blood seemed to freeze in her veins. For only now did she fully realise that she had been holding on to a glimmer of hope that a miracle would save her. She now knew that nothing could possibly save her, and with the knowledge came a feeling of lethargy to mingle with the resignation and she was able partly to relax.

'I suppose,' she replied in a very tired voice, 'that it doesn't matter one way or the other.'

Silence. She looked up to see a heavy frown creasing his forehead.

And then his mouth was tight and he was the ruthless predator again, bent on mischief.

He went to the door and held it open for her; she passed through, then stood aside and he preceded her up the stairs.

'We're in here—' He flung wide a bedroom door and she saw that the room was beautifully furnished with antiques and that the bed was a double one. 'This is the room I usually have when I'm here on a visit to my friends.'

Without a word Melanie went past him and into the room. He disappeared and came back a few moments later carrying a flimsy nightgown and matching overgown.

'You've—been into—into your friend's wardrobe?'

'We'll make sure all is put right before we leave,' was all Vidas said to that.

As if in a dream Melanie found herself accepting the articles of clothing offered.

'The bathroom's there.' He pointed and she moved towards it, a vacant expression on her face. 'Don't keep me waiting too long,' he advised as she reached the door, 'or I shall be tempted to come and fetch you out.'

Temper flared but she controlled it. She looked for a bolt on the door and realised that as it was an *en suite* bathroom there had been no need for one. She stood for a while, listening to sounds from the bedroom. How could a man be so calmly serene about the dastardly act he was about to commit? But then he was a Greek, and they were notorious world over for their devotion to the physical pleasures of life. Sex appeared to be the most important pastime of all—

'I'll use the bathroom when you've finished.'

Melanie's mouth went tight. If that was meant to hurry her up then he was in for a disappointment!

'I'm used to taking my time,' she snapped. 'Perhaps there's another bathroom you can use.'

'Perhaps there is.'

Melanie listened and heard him moving about for a bit longer and then there was silence. When she emerged he was standing by the window looking out into the darkness of the grounds. He was in a dressing-gown but a swift glance downwards told her that he was not wearing pyjamas. Her mouth felt dry and rough; her heart was pounding wildly against her ribs. Silently she cursed her sister for the first time, and she felt something akin to hatred for the father she had always loved. There they all were, sublimely ignorant of this ordeal she was enduring just so that they could enjoy peace of mind. Suddenly she wanted to know what had happened and she said, forgetting that the phone might be tapped,

'I'd like to ring my sister, if you don't mind?'

A frown knit his brows as he swung around to face her.

'Playing for time?' He shook his head slowly from side to side, while his darkly sensual glance took in the enchanting contours of her slender, youthful figure revealed by the transparency of the nightgown and its equally delicate overgown which, in any case, had no fastening to secure its front edges together. Melanie had brushed her hair and it shone in the rose-tinted glow from a solitary light by the bed, for already Vidas had dispensed with the main light which he had switched on when they entered the room.

'It isn't playing for time,' she began when he interrupted her.

'No? Well, whatever it is you have to say can wait until the morning. . . .' He was moving towards her as he spoke, moving with that athletic grace she had noticed before. Tall, and with that air of distinction that brands the nobility, he seemed so far above her, so god-like, that she wondered how he could stoop to bother about her, a mere mortal.

His intense gaze was as disconcerting as his next words,

'What are you thinking about, Melanie?'

'If you want the truth,' she replied without pause, 'I was wondering how a man like you could be interested in anyone like me. Obviously I'm far beneath you,' she added, and saw his frown appear again.

However, he made no comment on that but merely stopped in the middle of the floor and pointed to a spot at his feet.

'Come here,' he commanded softly. Melanie stayed where she was.

Into the silence the clock downstairs chimed the hour. Eleven. . . .

'I said, come here.' At the peremptory tone something snapped in Melanie's brain and her temper erupted like some volcanic explosion.

'Go to hell!' she gritted. 'I'm going to phone my sister! I *want* to phone my sister. I want to know what has happened!'

'You can guess what has happened.'

'No, I can't! I won't sleep if I don't find something out!'

The straight black brows lifted and the deep-set eyes took on an expression of mocking amusement.

'You're expecting to sleep?'

Melanie's small fists clenched.

'Play your cat and mouse game!' she blazed. 'And I hope it provides plenty of entertainment for that puerile mind of yours!' Even before he leapt across the room she knew she had gone too far, and she cursed herself for it. His face was a twisted mask of anger and when he spoke the words came as a snarling threat from between his teeth.

'You'll learn, my girl, that no one speaks to me like that and gets away with it!' His grip on her wrist brought forth a cry of pain and protest, but his crushing possession of her lips effectively stemmed anything further. He treated her body mercilessly and she felt those hawsers of steel would reduce her bones to pulp within seconds. She was so small and fragile in comparison to his size and the whipcord hardness of his body as it crushed hers. His hand wasted no time and she was soon aware of his exploration, his dominant and masterful possession of her breast with one hand and the removal of the overgown with the other. It fell to the floor around her feet; the action seemed to release the taut resistance she had put on her nerves and she started to cry, and to struggle at the same time. She managed to put a space between them and pummelled at his chest. He caught her hand and then the other, holding them imprisoned at her back and at the same time compelling her to arch her body to the shape of his. She felt the strength of his thighs, the urgency of his passion, the moist exploration of his mouth as it traced a line from the tender swell of her throat to the delectable curve of her shoulder, from where with his chin he had removed the strap of her nightgown.

At last he held her away from him after releasing her hands. She stood there, exhausted and weak, conscious of a tumult within her that left her without the inclination to resist, or even voice a protest when he flipped a ribbon at her throat which slackened the neckline of the nightdress. Both his hands were employed in removing the dainty garment, his fingers caressing her with slow deliberation as he bared her body inch by inch until she stood before him, naked and infinitely desirable. She averted her eyes; they became fixed on the nightdress at her feet, and she endeavoured by this absorption to ignore the hands which were slowly and sensuously smoothing their masterful way along her hips and thighs. But he was far too experienced for her; he knew every sensitive place and the effect his tactile questing would have upon her erotic nerves. A quiver of her body was the prelude to a tiny shock wave and he smiled the smile of a man arrogantly aware of his power over women. Melanie glanced up to see the triumph on his face change to one of sardonic amusement.

'No more objections, then? Didn't I say that you would not be disappointed? In a few minutes you will be happier than ever before in your life.' He swung her up into his arms and a spasm shuddered through her at the contact of his hands in intimate places. He laid her down on top of the covers, slipped out of his dressing-gown, and slid down beside her. To her surprise his hands were gentle when he touched her but his kiss was hard and moistly possessive. She parted her lips for him, obeyed when he told her to put her arms around him, made no protest when his teeth captured one hard pointed nipple and held it so that his tongue could tease and tempt with calculated finesse whose result was to bring her whole body to the point of surrender. She pressed against him, desiring now to feel his hard virility and thrill to it. Her fingers tangled themselves in his strong wiry hair, then lightly teased his nape and hypersensitive places behind his ears. She moved to feel the hard muscles of his chest, her body wrenching and arching as a paroxysm of urgent longing swept into her, ignited from the glowing embers of his own passion. She clutched at his flesh, gave a little moan when his long lean fingers curled round her lower curves to force her even closer to his loins.

Her senses reeled as rapture flowed through her like a warm stream of air blowing down from a tropical hillside. Her slender frame writhed under his caresses and suddenly he was on top of her.

'It might hurt a bit.' His voice, more noticeably accented than before, was vibrant with the passion that engulfed him.

'Yes. . . .' There was no protest, no fear . . . only eagerness and the desperate yearning for fulfilment. Tomorrow . . . the future . . . even the thought of prison one day . . . All were nothing in this moment of primitive passion that soon was to consume them both in an explosion of ecstasy.

It was the slamming of a car door that jerked them

to a state of immobility. Neither had heard the crunch of tires on gravel that preceded it.

'What the—!' Vidas sat up. The glow of headlights could be seen against the crimson velvet drapes. 'The Jeffersons! They've come back—Stephen and Hilary—' He broke off abruptly as a loud clang of the iron knocker thundered through the house. 'It isn't them.' He was out of bed; Melanie closed her eyes to the vision of the sinewed naked frame, then opened them again. She was burning inside and out, feverish with desire . . . and yet she ought by rights to have welcomed this diversion for it could just mean that she was saved.

'Can you see anything?' A silly question when those lights were still flaring, even more so now that Vidas had pulled back the drapes an inch or two.

'It's the police back again.' His voice was grim and tight.

'Th-the police?' Terror effectively brought back sanity and all sexual desire fled. 'What—I mean, will they w-want to search the house?' She was off the bed now and running towards the chair on which she had put her clothes. Vidas was getting into his dressing-gown.

'Stay where you are,' he commanded. 'Make no sound—'

'But I could run out the—the back way. . . .' Her voice trailed as she saw his expression.

'Do as you're told!' he snapped. 'I'll deal with them.'

A low curse escaped him when the clanging echoed through the house again.

'Can't they wait!' He was at the door and through

it. He closed it softly behind him and, noticing a key, Melanie went and turned it. Then she put on her clothes and sat on the edge of the bed. But she couldn't keep still and she went to the window and gently lifted the sash.

'I'm afraid you can't, as it isn't my house. The owners are away. However, I can assure you that no one is hiding in here.'

'With all due respect, sir, you couldn't know for sure. It looks to be a big place and we always find these types of house have many doors and windows, and so—'

'I have said, once and for all, that you can't come in. It isn't my house!'

There was a long silence then and Melanie waited with her breath caught in her throat for the men to get into the car and go away. It seemed an eternity before they did so but at last she heard the car doors close, the engine start and the purr as the car slid away along the drive. She ventured to peep through the curtains and saw the shape of the car and its rear lights melt into the inky blackness beyond the bend in the drive.

The rattle of the doorknob brought her round with a start.

The door was locked against her captor. . . .

'Open up!' Brief the order and imperious. Melanie trembled on the brink of indecision. 'Girl, unlock this door—or else.'

She obeyed and he entered, then stood staring down into her wide, limpid gaze. Then he threw back his head and laughed.

'You had nothing to fear,' he assured her. 'An

interruption like that, at a time like that—well, it sort of puts a guy off.'

She looked away. He shot out a hand to force her face round again, and another light laugh escaped him.

'Console yourself, my woman, there'll be plenty more opportunities.'

She coloured up but said nothing. In any case, Vidas, suddenly brisk, was already saying, firmly but not with undue urgency,

'It's best that we leave tonight, Melanie. Their coming back has convinced me that they'll be here again at dawn. They seemed convinced that you'd managed to get into the house and are hiding. They've been alerted about the theft. We must leave.'

'Tonight?' she gasped. 'But where—how—?'

'Again, just leave everything to me. Go down and make some coffee while I get dressed—and keep well away from any windows.'

'Yes. . . .' She looked at him and he smiled. A tense moment passed and then she managed a little smile herself. Vidas gave her a pat.

'Off you go,' he said, and she obeyed.

She was in the kitchen making the coffee when it dawned on her that it was rather pleasant and comforting to have someone say, as Vidas had said so confidently,

'Just leave everything to me.'

Chapter Four

The road was a delight of shady patios and sunlit squares, flower-bedecked and tranquil.

A village, taking up several hill-slopes, had its various areas connected by winding steps of natural limestone.

'It's all so beautiful,' breathed Melanie. 'Every little village seems to be unique, quite different from the others in its own particular way.'

'So you like my island?'

'I like what I've seen, yes, of course I do.'

Vidas, sitting beside her in the back of the chauffeur-driven car, turned his dark head to regard her in profile.

'It'll be your home from now on.'

'For how long, I wonder?'

'No one can predict the future,' he said gravely.

'Live for the present, my child. The past is dead for you; the future has yet to be born, so the time is surely now.'

She turned her head, sure that he was quoting. Yet it was true all the same . . . the time was now. She had become resigned, and she supposed it was because there really was nothing else she could do with any degree of safety.

'It's hard to believe that we made it without any trouble at all,' she mused, catching sight of the lovely waxy flowers of a pomegranate tree flaring in the hedgerow. 'I felt, when you phoned to have a taxi come last night at that late hour, that the police would be hiding in their car a few yards away and we'd find ourselves taking part in one of those chases you see in the films.'

'I'd been out and reconnoitred, remember, while we were waiting for the taxi.'

'Do you suppose he thought it suspicious that you asked him to wait along the road instead of coming right to the house?'

'Taxi drivers are used to people doing odd things,' was all Vidas had to say to that.

'The hotel in London . . . I daresay they thought it strange, arriving at that time. It was after two o'clock in the morning.'

'We'd just arrived off an airplane. I told you what I'd said. They're used to it. It happens all the time in any big city. What might have seemed strange was your arrival without even a bit of hand luggage. However, hotel staff are not there to hold inquests on their guests.' Arrogance entered into his voice and Melanie was more curious than ever to see where he lived and how he conducted his life. He had told her, on the plane coming over this morning, that in addition to his villa on Thristos, he had an apartment in Athens where he stayed when in the capital on business. He had surprised her several times, and not least was when she heard him ask for two rooms at the hotel in London. True, they were to be there for only a few hours, because their plane left at nine o'clock, but she had fully expected him to take only one room. He had said, though, with a hint of that sardonic amusement to which she was fast becoming used,

'Don't let yourself indulge in any false optimism, Melanie. This respite doesn't mean that I have changed my mind.' The dark foreign eyes had burned as they travelled over her. 'I still find you exceedingly desirable, hence your good fortune in my taking you under my protection.'

She had wisely made no comment, but she did think that the use of the word 'protection' savoured of something quite out of date.

There had been many chances of her making her escape but, motivated by something far stronger than herself, the idea, though considered, was never taken seriously. She gave as the explanation the fact of her having comparatively little money, no job or home, and last but by no means least, she would always be 'on the run'. And it was on the cards that she would inevitably be run to earth. Whereas, here in Greece, she was safe for the present—for as long as Vidas wanted her as his mistress. By the time he tired of her, she decided with a sort of cold-blooded philosophy, she would have saved more money and

she might be able to settle herself in a small apartment, perhaps in Athens, and get a job. The thought
of never returning to her own country was thrust
aside, since 'never' at her age was a long time. She
rather thought that, subconsciously, she was opti-
mistically taking for granted that one day in the
unforeseeable future 'something might happen'.
That was, something that would make it possible for
her to go back. Meanwhile, she was beginning to
accept that things might not be so bad after all.
Vidas might be a ruthless and formidable man, but
at least his love-making would not be of the kind that
was unbearable. Already she admitted that something about him attracted her; she unashamedly
accepted, too, that it was a purely physical attraction. Hitherto she had never regarded herself as
what was termed 'sexy'. But she now realised that
she hadn't met anyone anything like the Greek, with
his exceptional male magnetism and perfection of
face and figure. She knew without any doubt whatsoever that she could not, under any circumstances,
have agreed to his proposal if she hadn't felt anything about him at all. What she felt had come to her
right at the start, at that very moment when she had
run into his arms and clutched his shirt in a way
which made her vitally aware of him as a man. Yes,
he possessed a draw for her and it was the kind of
draw which she accepted not only philosophically
but with a sort of sublime resignation which had
miraculously erased most of her fears.

That the situation was unreal was something to be
considered, but on the other hand, it *was* in many
ways a very real situation, but one in which she

seemed to have been invested with a strange and inexplicable reserve of mental capacity where she was able to examine the crisis with cool objectiveness by which she was led to the firm and final conclusion that there was absolutely no acceptable alternative to the proposal Vidas had made to her. And because this acceptance had been forced upon her by motives both honourable and selfless, she knew no feelings of guilt or shame as to her morals. Had she possessed eight thousand pounds she would willingly have handed it over to her adoptive father in gratitude for all he had done for her; but as it was, she had been forced by circumstances to choose another way.

'You're very quiet.' He broke the silence at last and she turned her head.

'I was going over it all,' she told him frankly.

'And what is "it all"?' he wanted to know.

'Everything that has happened to me.'

'Your attitude suggests you haven't any regrets about the course you chose.'

'It was the only way.' Her voice was soft, resigned. He regarded her in profile, saw the beauty and desirability of her. And he wondered just how long this one would last.

She spoke again, a sigh in her voice.

'Thank you for the clothes,' she said.

'There's no need for gratitude. It's all part of the payment.'

She did blush then, and feel a tinge of embarrassment.

'I thought it was I who was paying you,' she murmured.

Vidas ignored that as he said,

'Athens is a good place to shop. I'm glad you were able to get all you needed in the time you had. Perhaps I rushed you a little, but I wanted to be out of Piraeus in time to reach Thristos before dark.'

'It was a lovely sail.' They had passed several islands and Vidas had pointed them out as Aegina, Poros and Hydra. He had also pointed out the hills of the Peloponnesus. There was plenty for her to see and do in Greece, he had said, rather casually, she thought, as if telling her she would have lots of time for herself.

Thristos had been reached at last, after a most enjoyable crossing, and Melanie was giving a little gasp of appreciation as the graceful white yacht drifted into the harbour, manned by Yannis and Pavlos who had been alerted to be ready to sail by early afternoon. The beautiful curvature of the bay of Thristos seemed to be alive with bright *caique*s or other fishing boats. On the shore men were mending their nets or slapping octopuses on the flagstones to create the lather which tenderises them. Hills rose in an arc behind the waterfront, thickly wooded hills where tiny villages nestled, and here and there the dazzling white campanile of a church glittered in the slanting rays of a golden, setting sun.

Vidas's low-slung white car was waiting, complete with a chauffeur in immaculate royal blue uniform and peaked cap. He was introduced to Melanie as Davos and when he smiled it was to reveal several bright gold fillings of which—it was more than plain—he was exceedingly proud. A dark-skinned stocky man, he had been with the Loudaros family for seventeen years, having worked for Vidas's father until his death four years ago. Like the two men crewing the yacht, he had at first stared curiously at his employer's companion and Melanie had felt herself go red.

'It's plain what they are all thinking,' she said with a frown when she and Vidas were in the car.

'Perhaps not quite what you suppose. They're puzzled at my bringing you to my home. You see,' he went on in that attractive foreign voice, 'this is the very first time I have brought one of my pillow-friends to my home. I usually conduct my affairs in Athens, in any case,' he added reflectively.

'But you have a reputation here on Thristos?'

He shrugged his shoulders.

'I expect so,' he replied equably.

'But you don't care?' What would people think of her? she wondered. Only now was this aspect of her situation occurring to her.

'No,' replied Vidas with a strange inflection in his voice now, 'I do not care.'

She had fallen silent, enjoying the journey from the quayside up into the hilly countryside where, quite often, artists were to be seen by the roadside, busy with brush and canvas. Sometimes the aspect would become faintly sombre where the umbrella pines predominated, but for the most part the scenery was characterised by flowering trees and bushes—the lovely oleanders along the banks of a stream, the flaring hibiscus forming glorious hedges of dazzling crimson or soft and subtle pink-peach. Jasmine, too, formed hedges, and above them were often to be seen the delightful jacaranda trees. From *tavernas* along the way *bouzouki* music, sad and evocative, drifted in through the open windows of the car, and once or twice Melanie saw men dancing, handkerchiefs linking them to one another as they leapt and gyrated high into the air, often in abandoned sexual movements, especially of the groin. Such a dance was being performed outside a *cafeneion* when the car happened to be held up by a man with a donkey, a dog, and two goats following slowly, led by his black-robed wife. Vidas, noticing Melanie's embarrassment, gave a short laugh and merely remarked,

'You'll get used to it. The Greeks have a reputation for giving vent to amorous impulses at the least opportunity.'

Melanie shook her head but said nothing; she had no wish that this man should keep deriving amusement at her expense.

When eventually the villa was reached via a long drive lined with waving dome palms, Melanie found herself gasping again. For the low white and blue building was a delight to the eye, and at once convinced her that the owner was a millionaire— probably several times over. Luxury was in evidence everywhere, from the entrance drive itself with its high, wrought-iron gates flanked by Doric-style pillars, to the sweeping lawns and sunken flower beds, the ornamental pool fed by a sparkling cascade which gushed out from the limestone, and so was a natural spring. Flowering shrubs and trees abounded, hedges of hibiscus and oleander, terraces and parterres. . . . All these she saw in the golden-bronze glow of a sun now sinking rapidly behind the tree-clothed hills to the west, and then the house was there, white and spreading with a forecourt banked with flowers and a glimpse of a shady courtyard to the left. Patios and balconies to every window, all with flowers growing in decorative urns of bronze and brass and locally made *jardinieres*.

The door was opened even before Melanie and Vidas were out of the car, and Vidas, with all the self-confidence to which Melanie was already used, introduced her to his manservant, Nico, whose smile revealed the inevitable gold fillings.

'*Kalispera sas*—good evening to you, *Kiria* Melanie.'

'Good evening . . . Nico.' Shyness flooded over and when she lifted her eyes to those of Vidas she surprised a most odd expression in his.

'You have the room ready?' Vidas spoke in English and the man nodded and answered in good but very broken English.

'I haf Stella do it for the lady, Mr. Vidas.'

Melanie was staring about her, taking in with wide, appreciative eyes the arch at the end of the hall, its Doric columns dripping with flowers growing in massive bronze urns, the mosaic floor with several Persian carpets placed here and there, the tapestries on the walls, and the paintings. One or two ikons were all that stamped anything Greek into it, for the chests and chairs were all English and of the Regency period.

'Why isn't Stella here—' Vidas broke off as a tall slender girl with dusky skin and rather sad eyes came hurrying from somewhere at the end of the hall. Presumably it was the kitchen, thought Melanie who, as she stood there amid all this splendour, experienced again that feeling of unreality.

It seemed impossible that this time yesterday she was sitting at a typewriter in her office, troubling herself about her father and mother but in total ignorance of the momentuous happenings that were to take place within the next twenty-four hours.

'Pardon, *kirios,*' she said hastily. 'My baby—he cry! I think he haf of the aching teeth.'

Baby . . . ? Swiftly Melanie's eyes darted to the tall man beside her. She saw his eyes take on a glimmer of humour and went red.

'No,' he said softly, close to her ear, 'I did say I hadn't any—that I knew of.' Laughter was the progression of the amusement in his gaze. Melanie turned away. What had caused her surprise was something quite different from what he had been so quick to surmise. Melanie had been surprised that Vidas was allowing this housemaid to keep her baby here. It did not seem that she was married, since she wore no ring. And that sad expression added strength to Melanie's deductions.

'Take *Kiria* Melanie to her room.' His voice was cool and imperious. 'You can then have Souphoula telephone the doctor to come and see your baby. I think you'll find that she's cutting her teeth, as you say, and is in pain.'

'Thank you, *Kirios*—Mr. Vidas.' She glanced at Melanie with a curious expression and then gestured. She seemed shy and Melanie wished she could find something to say to put her at her ease.

'This ees the room, *Kiria* Melanie.'

'Thank you.'

83

'Do you wish it that I do something for you?'

'Not just now.' Then Melanie added as the girl reached the door, 'Who is Souphoula?'

'The cook. She very good. And she the—what you say?—the keeper of the house?'

'The housekeeper,' smiled Melanie and the girl managed a thin smile in response.

'How long have you worked for Mr. Vidas?'

'One year and a half. He hear from Nico that I make baby with bad man he say for me to come here, for, you see, my father tell me to go—it is the disgrace.' Tears welled up in the lovely dark eyes and swiftly Stella brushed them away.

'Mr. Vidas was very good to you.'

'Very good, yes! He very much look after peoples who are in troubles.'

Melanie looked at her in silence, conscious of a new and profound emotion, and of an excess of puzzlement, too, for it did seem that the man whom she knew as a rake, a ruthless womaniser, had an altogether different side to his personality.

'And how old is your baby now?'

'She just one year olds.'

'I shall love to see her,' said Melanie with a smile.

'Tomorrow?' The dark eyes lit up. 'I show her to you, *Kiria* Melanie, and you will think she is a very—what you say?—pretty little girl?'

'I'm sure she is pretty, Stella.' Suddenly the girl was looking over Melanie's shoulder and, frowning, she swung around.

'Oh!'

'I go,' said Stella swiftly and almost shot through the door.

'I didn't realise that—that there was a door there,'

stammered Melanie, conscious of the satirical smile curving Vidas's lips. 'I hadn't had time to look around.'

He was in the open doorway and she could glimpse the room beyond.

'You surely expected to have me close?' The smile became broader and Melanie felt her temper rise.

'I suppose so,' she snapped, 'but I can't see anything amusing about it!'

He came forward and reached out to take her hands in his. She was drawn close, her face tilted, and for a long moment he stared down into her face, an odd expression on his own. Something inside her quivered, like a tingling of nerves; she did not know why she should be thinking of Stella and her baby at this time but she was.

'You're a hot-tempered woman,' he stated, but in mild tones. 'This suite is for the master of the house and his wife. My parents used it until Mother died and then Father couldn't bear to stay in his room.'

'You make it sound as if it were a love match,' she said, still forced to look up into his face by the firm hand beneath her chin.

'It was a love match.'

'I thought Greeks never bothered about love. I was under the impression that marriages were always arranged.'

He shook his head and released her.

'Not always. My parents' marriage was arranged, though. But they were fortunate; they fell in love and stayed that way.'

'Your father was faithful—?' She cut abruptly, colouring up at her lack of tact.

'You may not believe it,' he said with some

amusement, 'but my father was a very good-living man. He did not favour loose morals.'

'Then you must have been a bitter disappointment to him,' she could not resist retorting.

'I was,' admitted Vidas, and his face changed so that harsh lines marred the classical good looks she had so admired and which had affected her in a way she had never known before with any other man.

'And you didn't care that you were hurting him?'

'I cared, yes, but once a man embarks on the wrong path it's not easy to turn back.'

Melanie shot him a glance. A hint of an amused smile had erased the harshness from his face within seconds.

'I believe you're teasing me,' she accused and then thought that this was a rather peculiar conversation for them to be having. Perhaps he thought so too because he tilted her face again, bent his head, and kissed her hard on the mouth.

'What a piece of luck when you were thrown in my way,' he said after a long while. 'And for you it's lucky—'

'You think so?' Her eyes sparkled. 'You are a pompous man, Vidas, full of your own importance.'

'And you, my girl,' he responded in a very soft and dangerous tone, 'are imprudent to say the least.'

'You're threatening me?' How daring would she get? she wondered, recalling with a shock that this time yesterday this man was unknown to her!

'Don't tempt me,' he warned in the same quiet voice. 'I have a somewhat formidable temper.'

'I'll try not to rouse it,' she promised tartly. He shook her but not roughly.

'You know,' he murmured, subjecting her to a piercing scrutiny, 'it seems impossible that we've known one another for rather less than twenty-four hours.'

'I was thinking the same myself. It's hardly credible.'

'That we've become so familiar?'

She averted her face.

'You were saying that I'm lucky,' she said in order to change the subject. 'In what way, exactly?'

'In several ways, but the main one is that, for the time being, you'll have the good life, whereas if you'd been at home—and the present problem apart—there would have been every possibility of your meeting someone from the office, marrying him, and being glued to a square yard of floor beneath the kitchen sink.'

'You're a cynic,' she accused. 'Marriage for a woman isn't all drudgery.'

'You obviously believe in love and romance.' Sardonic humour edged his voice and his eyes were searching.

'I did,' she murmured almost to herself.

'Did?'

'It isn't much use now, is it? I can't marry anyone after—after . . .' She trailed off to an embarrassed silence and even yet again she felt his lean fingers beneath her chin, tilting it in that masterful way he had.

'Do you really suppose, these days, that it'll matter if you've had an affair? It would be a strange sort of man who would cast you down for that. In any case, he needn't know.' Vidas gave her no time for a comment as he bent to take her lips again. 'You're altogether too tempting when you look at me like that,' he said, and it did seem that his voice was a trifle thick. 'How is it that you weren't married years ago?'

'Years? I'm only twenty-one; I told you that.'

'It's a wonder you weren't discovered when you were seventeen, or even younger.'

'Perhaps I was.' She drew away from him and looked at her shiny new suitcase, bought only a few hours ago in Athens. Inside were some very lovely dresses and underwear and shoes.

'You were? But you've never had an affair, you said.'

'Not anything remotely serious. I've been out with boys, but I haven't ever met the man I could settle down with.' Her eyes were drawn from the case to his dark features and she knew a bewildering sensation of warmth in the region of her heart. She blinked, a little dazed at not being able to put an instant finger on the reason. She could still feel his kisses, the touch of his hand beneath her chin, the warmth of his hands when he had taken hold of her arms just now and shaken her.

'You will, and it could be a Greek; who knows?'

'I can't think a Greek would want to marry me. They always want chaste girls for brides.'

'Perhaps not so much these days.' He paused a moment. 'I think we had better be getting ready for dinner. Souphoula's cooking is too good to let spoil.'

Melanie glanced at the open door behind him.

'You—I . . .' She had no idea what she wanted to say.

'This room,' was his bland rejoinder. And then, looking at her with an unfathomable expression, 'You seem very calm about it now.'

She passed her tongue over her lips.

'I accept what fate has dictated.'

'That makes two of us.' He drew her close and his arms were gentle around her. 'Fate plays very strange tricks,' he added cryptically. 'It brought us together in the most improbable circumstances.'

She nodded her head, vitally aware of him as a man . . . and of the indisputable fact that she wanted him to kiss her.

Her lips were moist and inviting; he smiled enigmatically and bent his head. She felt his cool clean breath fanning her throat, his fingers pressing into her waist, his body coming close to meld itself with hers. The heady sensation of pleasure in store seemed to rob her of any thought other than his nearness, his masculinity . . . his power to take her to rapturous heights. Last night she had been but a dream away from paradise and she knew it. Tonight . . .

'Put your arms around my neck.' His strong accented voice brought immediate obedience. She thrilled to the awareness that she too could give pleasure as she felt his body ripple under the stimulation of her tactile explorations.

He kissed her with a kind of pagan ardour, fierce and burning, and yet, somehow, there was a subtle tenderness in the demand of his lips, a gentle persuasion in their conceited mastery. His hands were active but gentle, coercive but teasing, and tantalising in a way that sent a fevered surge of longing into every erotic cell of her body. She wanted him with every part of her, craved to be possessed by this pagan Greek, this self-confessed rake whose experience with numerous other women was being employed so effectively on her at this moment.

But nothing mattered, not her own idealistic beliefs nor the fact that Vidas was the last man any self-respecting woman should have willingly surrendered to.

'Melanie. . . .' His voice was rough and thick against the vulnerable hollow of her throat. 'I have never made love to anyone as seductive, as desirable as you.'

She clung to him, arching her slender form to his shape, finding rapture in the knowledge of his need of her. Other women . . . yes. But now he was interested in *her alone* . . . and the question of how long she could hold that interest was as unimportant at this moment in time as the dinner he had previously mentioned.

However, he managed to draw away from her and she heard his ragged uneven breathing gradually settle. She felt weak in her legs, a trembling throughout her body, and it was as if he in his wide experience knew exactly how she felt and that she needed his supporting hands for a moment or two.

'Have you recovered?' he asked eventually and she frowned at him.

'Are you making fun of me?' She had no idea why

that should have been voiced, for there was no sign of the familiar curve of sardonic amusement about his lips. 'It wasn't a very tactful question to ask.'

'Do we need to be tactful with each other?' His hands were gentle on her arms, gentle and warm and supporting.

'I'll get ready,' she almost snapped and Vidas gave a low laugh and kissed her lightly on the lips.

'Disappointment?'

Melanie coloured to the roots of her hair.

'You have the kind of inflated ego that I detest!' was her swift and furious rejoinder.

She fully expected some form of reprisal but to her surprise he laughed.

'We're almost like an old married couple.' His second surprise was the touch of his hand on her hair, then the feel of strong fingers combing through its silky mass. 'But we're not, are we? On the contrary, we're newly-met lovers-to-be, both impatient to get into bed together.'

Her teeth snapped as her temper rose, and it was no help to be admitting that what he said was absolutely true.

What had happened to her in that vital moment when she had dashed her escaping body against him? Something ignored at first in the panic of being chased by the police, but very soon being thrust into her consciousness, and accepted. And undoubtedly it had played at least some part in influencing her as to the decision she had made, for she now knew without any shadow of doubt that, if he had been a man abhorrent to her, she could never have made that decision.

Was she falling in love with him? The shock of the question put a startled look into her eyes and she saw that Vidas's were narrowing slowly as he watched her. Still shaken by that question she found herself facing another: had she fallen in love with him on sight—at that moment of contact? This was too crazy an idea and she pushed it to the back of her mind.

He seemed to be waiting for some response to his words and she said, with the sort of unconscious appeal that brought a strange, unfathomable expression to his face,

'I suppose you despise me for—for agreeing to your proposal.'

'Don't be absurd. You know full well I don't despise you. On the contrary, I am almost inclined to admire you. However, you *are* a thief, and that is something I cannot condone.'

She turned aside, half wishing she had told him the full story, since she was feeling a sudden weight of dejection at the knowledge that he believed her to be dishonest. She could of course tell him now that she wasn't guilty, but she could scarcely expect him to believe her. In fact, he would despise her for trying to put the blame on her sister.

'I had better get ready,' she said again, a sigh in her voice. 'Do I put on the long dress you said I must buy?'

'Of course. Dinner is a social occasion and one should dress for it.' He was suddenly very correct and rather arrogant. 'Laziness these days is robbing us of the more special things of life. Dress designers should cash in and bring about a revival of the long dress for dancing and dining.' He turned back into his room and said over his shoulder, 'We're dining at about nine o'clock. And I am not happy if I'm kept waiting.'

Melanie glowered at the closed door. Did he need to be so darned pompous and dictatorial!

Chapter Five

There was an impassive expression on the face of Vidas as Melanie entered the crepuscular dimness of the elegant dining-room. It was lit merely by candles and the light of the full moon intruding through the wide high window, over which the drapes had not been drawn. A fountain played at the far end of the lawn, its marble cupid silhouetted against a dark background of cypress trees. For a moment Melanie stood by the door, looking rather like a Gainsborough portrait in her long, full-skirted dress of taffeta, its tight-fitting bodice hugging her breasts and accentuating the tiny waist. The colour was of a shade between cerulean and sapphire, so flattering to her eyes and hair.

Vidas had put on a tape and the strains of Dvorak's *New World* Symphony was quietly filling the room. Her eyes flicked around in swift examination of its decor and its contents, and she was again struck by the atmosphere of cultured good taste and the strong impression of artistic flair. The furniture was French, with the dining chairs covered in cerise-and-gold satin and the lovely patina of age on the table, where starched hand-embroidered mats took the place of a tablecloth. Matching napkins were folded to an intricate pattern. Crystal glasses for water and more slender ones for champagne, gleaming antique silver, white orchids with bright green foliage in the centre of the table and mauve ones at each cover looking as if they were actually growing in their tiny Chelsea-Derby cups.

'You look beautiful.' The compliment reached her above the music and she came forward, profoundly aware of this unreal world into which Katie's action had landed her. This room was sheer magic . . . and the man was like a scion of ancient Greek nobility . . . or a prince.

'Thank you,' she murmured and looked down at the carpet, feeling inexpressibly shy and inadequate. Then she felt his hands curling around her face, his lips lightly brushing hers.

'I did a good night's work, I'm thinking.' Although there was a sort of mocking humour in his voice, his eyes when he looked into hers were serious. 'We shall do very well together, Melanie, and have no fear for the future; I shall see that you are well provided for.'

The future . . . when he no longer wanted her. This was what he was referring to and Melanie swallowed the lump that had risen in her throat.

'Thank you,' she said again in almost inaudible tones.

His mouth curved. He moved away from her and she stared past him to where the clouds could be seen banking over the sea.

'Do you like this music?' he asked with a faintly lingering smile.

She nodded her head, quite unaware that the movement brought to his notice the beauty of her hair as it caught the amber candleglow and the silver from the moon. But she did see the slight pulsation of a nerve in his throat, and wondered at it.

'Yes, very much.'

'I'm glad, for I'd not want to bore you.'

Surprise widened her eyes but she made no comment. Vidas moved with that particular grace towards a bell-rope and pulled it.

'We are ready to eat now,' he said quietly when Nico came to the door.

'Yes, Mr. Vidas.'

'He doesn't always call you Mr. Vidas.' Melanie sent him a puzzled look.

'It's rather more for your sake,' was all he said, and brought out a chair for her. His chin brushed the top of her head and a quiver of emotion passed through her.

There seemed to be a change in him from what he was like at first, in England. He had said he didn't despise her for her decision to become his mistress so perhaps he was now beginning to have a little respect for her.

He certainly treated her with gallantry during the entire meal, passing her the bread rolls or the butter, asking if the fillet of beef en croûte was done to her liking and, later, if Pavlova with raspberries was to her taste.

'I have never had such a wonderful meal,' she told him naively when they had finished and Vidas had told Nico they would have their coffee in the living-room. 'It was delicious.'

He seemed pleased at her enjoyment of the meal and again she found herself puzzled by the enigma of his changed attitude towards her. Strange man! She wanted to understand him and wondered if she would be here long enough to do so.

They hadn't been in the living-room more than ten minutes when Nico knocked discreetly and opened the door in response to Vidas's call,

'Come in.'

'Miss Oliver is here. . . .' He shot a glance at Melanie and seemed decidedly uncomfortable. Melanie felt a tingling along her spine when she saw Vidas's expression, for his mouth was tight, almost evil, and the dark eyes were narrowed to mere slits. There was a fractional pause and then he said in an impassive tone,

'Show her in here, Nico.'

'Yes, Mr. Vidas.' He withdrew and again Melanie looked at Vidas, questioningly this time.

'A friend,' he vouchsafed imperturbably. She felt sure he didn't mean it.

'English?'

'That wasn't too difficult to deduce,' came his faintly sarcastic rejoinder.

Melanie coloured slightly and retorted before she gave herself time to think,

'One of your—er—pillow-friends?'

The basalt eyes glinted.

'Be very careful,' he warned in a dangerously soft voice. 'You go too far, girl!'

Her colour deepened, and at that moment a tall, dark-haired girl came into the room and Nico closed the door behind her. She had been looking at Vidas and started to say helló when her eyes lit on Melanie and she gave a start of what could only be described as shocked surprise.

'Vidas . . . who . . . ?'

'Come right in, Delia,' he invited with a thin smile. 'Meet Melanie—Miss Grayshott, a very dear friend of mine.'

'Dear friend?' The girl, beautiful and dressed with exquisite taste in a pale blue trouser suit, and with her gleaming hair immaculately taken back in a pleat, recovered her composure and was regarding Melanie with undisguised interest and hostility. What was Vidas about? wondered Melanie, feeling she wanted to get away from an atmosphere which could be cut with a knife. Dear friend. . . . 'You've never mentioned her to me.'

Ignoring that with pointed indifference, Vidas completed the introduction and Melanie found her hand taken in a cold and limp way that made her shudder. She disliked the girl on sight, but she was puzzled by the whole situation, and not least by the fact that the girl was English.

However, she managed to keep her tones polite as she offered the brief,

'How do you do, Miss Oliver.'

The girl merely nodded, her dark eyes glittering with a strange expression. To Melanie she seemed to be searching her mind for something she was anxious to recall. Her lids came down slowly after a few silent seconds and Melanie would have very much liked to know just what the girl's thoughts were. She was a deep one, decided Melanie, but beautiful, and for that reason she could imagine the girl being desirable as far as Vidas was concerned.

'I didn't expect a visit from you, Delia.' Vidas broke the silence, speaking in a hard but inquiring voice.

She sank elegantly into a chair and leant back against cushions.

'I heard you were back and thought I'd drop in.' She opened her handbag and brought forth a gold cigarette case. 'I had no idea you had a guest.'

'How did you know I was back? News seems to travel fast on Thristos,' he added with cold sarcasm.

'A friend phoned a couple of hours ago for a chat. She was at the *cafeneion* on the harbour when your yacht sailed in.' The girl shot Melanie a glance. 'She wouldn't know you were bringing a visitor with you.' If Melanie was curious about the girl it was nothing to the curiosity with which Delia was regarding her. Again that moment of concentration as if she were endeavouring to recall something.

Vidas said,

'How is your father?'

'Much the same. We're hoping he'll recover but are not banking on it. The attack was severe.'

Vidas took up his coffee cup and drained it. He was thoughtful and his face was oddly harsh.

'You'll be seeing him tomorrow?'

'Of course; we can see him anytime we want.'

'If he's conscious, give him my regards.'

Delia looked suspiciously at him as if in doubt as to the sincerity of the message to be relayed to her father.

'I will,' she returned briefly and then, after a pause, 'Can I speak with you alone, Vidas?'

He shook his head instantly.

'You would not expect me to leave my guest?'

The girl's mouth tightened. She rose from the chair.

'I'll give you a ring in the morning,' she almost snapped. 'Good night.'

'Good night.' Vidas rose and opened the door for her. As she passed him she whispered something and he accompanied her to the front door. Melanie heard her voice raised in anger,

'You'll live to regret it, Vidas! I'm not one of your poor little Greek girls, to be cast off when you've finished with them! I'm English—and if Father dies I'll be the owner of something you want badly. But there's only one way you're going to be able to get it!'

'By marrying you?' Although Vidas's voice was much quieter it came through to Melanie, sitting there, her coffee cup poised half-way to her mouth.

'You would have done once.' Anger had gone and Melanie felt sure the girl was now close to tears. 'What happened, Vidas?'

'Good night, Delia.' The snub was awful, thought Melanie, and suddenly she could feel sorry for the girl.

'I hate you—and I shall make you pay for this!'

The door closed and Vidas came back into the room. He stood looking at Melanie for a brief moment and then, walking casually over to his chair,

'You heard, obviously?'

'Yes, I heard.'

'And reached certain conclusions, I expect?' He sat down and hitched up a trouser leg.

'She was your—er—mistress. She owns the other half of this island—'

'Not half, nor even quite a quarter,' he corrected.

'Well, some of it.' She looked hard at him. 'You said you intended to get it.'

He nodded his head.

'I did tell you that, and I meant it.' His voice now had an harsh edge to it and his basalt eyes glittered. 'She doesn't own it yet,' he went on to add. 'Her father does, and he came by it in a way which I consider wasn't honest.'

Melanie looked at the harsh face and decided not to ask any questions, for she knew she would be snubbed, just as Delia had been. But something she could not control did make her ask,

'Were you really intending to marry her once?'

No answer and Melanie regretted the question, waiting for some caustic remark or reprimand. None came. Vidas glanced at the clock and said quietly,

'I don't know about you, but I'm ready for bed.' His voice now carried a hint of mocking amusement which was reflected in his eyes. She coloured and looked down at her hands, clasped tightly in her lap.

'We—hardly know each other,' she began, then was stopped by his laugh of sheer humour. He got up and moved towards her.

'Shy? You're rather refreshing. . . .' His voice trailed as he caught her wrist to bring her to her feet. 'Pity you're a thief,' he murmured.

'I—' Dared she tell him the truth? No, she was

101

still of the opinion that he would consider her to be lying. She had left it too long, and now she dared not make a full confession and have him despise her for trying to lay the blame on a girl unable to defend herself.

'You—what?' he prompted, watching her closely.

'Nothing,' she returned flatly.

'I suppose you consider yourself less guilty because of the motive for the theft,' he frowned.

She shook her head, an automatic gesture rather than a negative one.

'It's in the past and I'd like to forget it,' she murmured, her voice catching on a tiny sigh.

He bent his head and kissed her.

'Come,' he urged and she went with him to the door.

She was in a diaphanous nightgown when, twenty minutes later, Vidas came quietly into her room and closed the communicating door behind him. He stood regarding her for a long moment, the keen, deep-set eyes taking in everything, and stripping her at the same time. She coloured up and turned her head away. What had she done by agreeing to this? Surely there could have been some other way.

And yet she wanted him, desperately. She wondered what he would have to say if he learned she was in love with him.

A weight settled on her; she had the sensation of being on the rim of an abyss . . . into which she must inevitably fall, sometime, when this man had tired of her. She fell to wondering again about Delia and if he had at one time seriously considered marrying her. Surely not. For once married his other amorous activities would be curtailed . . . or would they? He was too attractive by far; always he would be pursued by women. And yet, as she lifted her limpid eyes to meet his gaze, she suddenly felt convinced that if ever—by some miracle—he did fall in love, he would from then on be faithful.

But where was there a woman who could win his heart?

'You're thoughtful,' he murmured, moving with that familiar grace across the room towards where she was standing, the light from the moon outside fashioning her body into delectable curves as it shone through the uncurtained window . . . and through the transparency of the nightgown.

'I suppose I'm a little . . . scared,' she confessed, yet lifted her face to the gentle touch of his finger beneath her chin, lifted it eagerly for his kiss.

His arms about her were strong, masterful, his lips hard and demanding, and yet there was a gentleness present in his every contact with her body. It was a long time before he held her from him and by this time her eyes were shaded and dreamy from his love-making. His eyes glittered with unslated desire as they travelled slowly over her from head to foot, devouring the beauty that lay beneath the shimmering folds of the nightgown.

'I'd hoped I had already convinced you there's nothing to be scared of,' he said in a belated comment on her confession. 'Are you still afraid?' he added interestedly, awaiting her reply.

She shook her head. He had most effectively aroused her to the point where longing, urgent and primitive, reigned over every other emotion.

'No, Vidas, I'm not afraid now.'

His long lean fingers were caressing the nape of her neck; she quivered as rapture began to swell within her, creating a blissful suffusion of warmth which in turn gave birth to the torment of longing, the fervid craving for fulfilment. His own need was more than apparent in the hardness she felt against her as he arched her pliable frame to meld with his. Melanie's arms came up in slow seductive progress to rest upon his shoulders . . . inside the dressing-gown he wore, the only garment. His lips in masterful possession seemed to be devouring hers; and then they were demanding and hard, coercing hers to part for him to explore the dark sweetness of skin like silk. She quivered with ecstasy, her head forced back, her body under his complete control as her curves were caressed through the inadequacy of its covering. The warmth of his hands was fuel to the fire of her longing; she felt an ache in her loins and pressed even harder against him, seeking for the final rapture of all. Every erotic cell within her was alive with unbearable heat and she failed to stem the little moan of entreaty that leapt to her lips,

'Love me . . . Vidas, love me. . . .'

His mouth had been softly caressing her throat, but at her words it claimed hers again in a kiss that left her gasping for breath. They were both caught in a storm of primitive violence, their bodies swaying, hands exploring, lips locked together. Vidas's body was hot against her, his hands almost cruel as they curled around her curves, one on her breast and the other tightly fastened to her thigh. His body was hot against her, his hand on her breast almost cruel in its lack of restraint, but the fingers possessing the nipple were pleasure-giving in spite of the pain, and the desperate ache in her loins increased to the agony of fevered desire.

'You're the most seductive, bewitching woman I've ever made love to!' His voice was almost strident with passion and the glitter in his eyes was like embers newly-fanned.

She hated the words of comparison but could not draw away and voice a protest. No, she had gone too far for any thought of turning back. Her hands were in his hair, then caressing his nape and behind his ears; she felt him quiver within the swaying movements of his frame, became aware of a hand lifting the hem of the nightgown. But then he decided it was in the way anyway and she stood unprotesting when he slid it from her shoulders, sliding his hands as well, so that the skin of her body tingled under the butterfly lightness of fingers deliberately—and knowledgeably—tempting as they caressed. She remained still when, with his hands on her arms, he held her from him so that his eyes could devour sensuously, and then they came to rest on her face, flushed now as she stood before him in her nakedness, a man who, thirty-six hours ago, had been unknown to her. And suddenly she grew rigid and her face paled.

'It's wrong,' she cried. 'I must have been out of my mind to agree! I'm now willing to go home and—and give myself up—'

'Stop!' ordered Vidas in sudden anger. 'What the devil do you think you're doing?' His eyes roving her body held contempt. 'The bargain's made, girl, and you shall be made to keep to it. There's a certain code of honour between . . .' For some reason he allowed his voice to trail away, and in the same instant a heavy frown knit his brows. Melanie said, tears stiffening her lashes,

'Between a profligate and a—'

'Don't say it!' he thundered, startling her. 'If you say it, girl, you'll be over my knee and screaming for mercy! I mean it!'

She stared, diverted from the awareness that she was totally unclothed. He was furious, and it was because she had been about to brand herself a no-good . . . give herself a name she would never have believed she could think of, much less voice. The man was an enigma, she decided, a man with several facets to his nature, and each was as puzzling as the next.

'I'm sorry. . . .' She had no idea why she should murmur the apology, unless it was that she desperately wanted him to lose his anger and be passionately loving with her again.

But instead he stooped to retrieve the nightgown. He held it out to her and ordered her to put it on, which she did, with clumsy, trembling hands. The tears came running down her cheeks and she wiped them away with the front of the nightgown, a gesture which caught and held his attention, a childish action that seemed in some unfathomable way to touch him deeply.

Vidas retied the cord of his dressing gown that had come loose. He stared down into her face and she noticed with wondering disbelief that a nerve was pulsating in his throat and, conscious of it, he pressed a finger against it.

'Go to bed.' His voice was abrupt and commanding. 'You're tired—and so am I. We've both had a gruelling twenty-four hours.' And with that he turned and strode towards the door which he had closed only half an hour ago. Reaching it, he turned to examine her face and to say, with that now-familiar hint of mocking amusement,

'I expect you feel as frustrated as I—' He shrugged and felt for the handle of the door. 'Another time,' he said with taunting satire, 'so don't feel too disappointed. I have no intention of changing my mind about our pact. You're far too captivating to be ignored.'

She stared, aware of a choking sensation in her throat, of the settling of a pounding heart . . . but also of an ache there, and the paradoxical feeling of relief and disappointment. . . .

She heard herself say quiveringly,

'Good night, Vidas.'

He laughed and said,

'I notice you haven't thanked me for my restraint.'

Colour fused her cheeks as anger rose.

'*You* might be frustrated,' she said cuttingly, 'but *I* am *not!*'

'Liar!'

'Did anyone tell you of your inflated ego?'

'Not until now,' he answered, the laughter still in those dark, basalt eyes of his. 'Aren't you curious as to the reason for my change of mind?' he added after a small silence.

She did not know how to answer—until an idea came to her.

'It could have been chivalry,' she said and let the heavy sarcasm come plainly through. 'Perhaps you are deciding to turn over a new leaf.'

Again he laughed and she caught her breath at the sheer attractiveness of him.

'But haven't I just warned you that I've no intention of changing my mind about the pact we made?'

'I wish I could understand you,' she cried peevishly.

'You might, one day, who knows?' was all he returned to that, and the next moment she was alone, staring at the closed door and feeling drained of all emotion—empty and with her mind chaotic.

But deep in her heart she knew what she had wanted, this despite the words she had hysterically uttered about having had a change of heart and now being willing to give herself up.

She wanted Vidas—oh, yes, with all that was in her she wanted him, the comfort of his nearness, the warmth of his body, the caress of his hands. She wanted to be possessed wholly, to know the world-shattering experience of the ecstasy which Vidas's triumph as the conqueror would have given her.

But instead she was alone, and weeping, and as she dwelt on her situation as an alien in a strange country, a fugitive from justice, she felt as if she wanted to die.

Chapter Six

The following morning she was awakened by the sun flooding the room, for she had forgotten to draw the curtains last night. The sun made everything seem so bright and warm that the dejection she had been kept awake by fell from her like a heavy weight discarded.

She sat up, strangely excited by the thought that she was in Greece, on the enchanting island of Thristos, a small island in the Saronic Gulf from where could be seen the islands of Aegina, as well as Poros, part of it pine-forested with sandy coves, similar to Thristos itself—so Vidas had told her as they sailed into the Gulf from Piraeus.

Her first dawn. . . . But actual dawning was a couple of hours ago at least, she decided, looking at the position of the sun.

She took a bath and felt even lighter in spirit; she glanced several times at the closed communicating door as she dressed, and wondered if Vidas was up yet.

She put on a short cotton dress she had bought in Athens and liked herself in it, the colour of jonquil trimmed with white on neckline and hem, looking fresh and summery and suiting her mood. She would not allow her mind to wander in backswitching recollections of last night; it was over and done with. Such was her present philosophy, which was the reason for her risen spirits. She brushed her hair till it glowed with health and colour, springing up at the ends which reached almost to her shoulders. White leather sandals completed the outfit and she wished she had perfume, and perhaps a bit of jewelry. So much left behind. Would she ever see any of her possessions again? Ever return to England? What was Katie doing and thinking at this moment? With a glance at the clock on the dressing table Melanie was seeing her sister hurrying over breakfast, for in ten minutes she would be hastening for the bus which would take her to the office. How had she coped with the scandal? Katie had as much as said she must not phone for some time but Melanie would not have been human if she hadn't been curious, too curious to refrain from telephoning her sister. Should she do it at her office, though? Perhaps this would be best, just in case the flat phone was being watched.

'I think I had better have Vidas's advice,' she was saying as she stepped out on to the balcony for a moment or two. It was rather pleasant to be able to ask someone's advice, she realised. Despite the love and care given by her adoptive parents she had never been able to 'lean' on them, she now realised. But she felt she could lean on the man who had saved her from the police and, probably, prison.

Vidas was already in the morning room when she entered, and Nico was there too, at the sideboard just having brought in a covered tray which he now was laying across two small spirit heaters. Vidas turned from his contemplation of the garden and the sea beyond, his dark eyes travelling over Melanie's frame and narrowing slightly as if he would hide his expression from her. Yet he did say when Nico had left the room,

'You look charming, Melanie. I'm glad I made you buy that dress. It is you, as I said at the time.'

Her mouth set at the word 'made'. Did he need to be so dictatorial!

'It's a lovely morning,' she said rather crisply.

'Most mornings are like this,' he said and, moving, he pulled out a chair for her and she sat down. He took the place opposite and rang a bell. Nico came back.

'You can serve now,' he said, and the servant went to him first.

'Miss Melanie.' The brief order was obeyed although Nico looked a trifle puzzled. It was plain that here in Greece the lord and master of the house was always served first. She had some fruit first and then grilled bacon with mushrooms and tomatoes. Vidas had the same and while they ate he opened a conversation, saying that although there were several good shops on the island, she would want to go to Athens for really stylish clothes.

'I don't need anything very stylish,' she was swift

to return. 'I expect I shall spend a good deal of my time here, in the garden, or on the beach.'

'I do entertain at times,' he told her.

'You'll want me—?' She shook her head. 'I don't want to meet people, Vidas.'

'Surely you must have known you'd be meeting my friends?'

'I didn't think—' Again she stopped, this time to give a small deprecating smile. 'There hasn't been much time for thinking, has there?'

Vidas shook his head, returning her smile.

'I think we must go to Athens within the next week or so,' he decided. 'I myself have some shopping to do.'

'I was wanting your advice,' said Melanie as she poured him a second cup of coffee.

'Yes?' His gaze was curious.

'About phoning my sister to see what is going on.'

'I had the impression from something you said that she wouldn't be expecting a phone call from you.'

'That's right. I wanted to phone last night but you wouldn't let me, and afterwards I knew it was wise not to. But I can't go on, not knowing what has transpired.'

'Woman's curiosity, eh?' Vidas helped himself to more toast.

'It's natural that I should want to know what's going on,' she retorted.

'You want my advice, you said?'

She nodded and he became thoughtful.

'Although I do want to phone I'm not sure whether it would be best to reach Katie at the office or at home.'

He was still lost in thought. Melanie buttered a piece of croissant and popped it into her mouth.

'If I were you,' said Vidas at last, 'I'd leave the phoning for a while—a week at least.'

'You would?' A frown knit her brow. 'For what reason?'

'The phones will be watched, no doubt of that. And calls can be traced even though they come from abroad.' He shot her a glance. 'You don't want to be arrested and taken back, do you?'

She shuddered and said no, she didn't want that, whereupon Vidas reminded her that only a few hours ago she told him she was ready to give herself up.

'I know I said that but I didn't mean it,' she confessed, and was not in the least surprised when he laughed.

'I rather think,' was his dry comment, 'that you often say things you don't mean.'

She coloured up, fully aware that he was obliquely referring to what she had so vehemently maintained last night: that she was not feeling frustrated.

'What do you do with yourself all day?' she asked, and it was with a little sensation of shock that she realised just how little she and this dark Greek knew of one another.

'I have a study in the house and work there for several hours daily—when I'm at home, that is. My main office is in Athens, where I employ eleven people including a manager, so I don't have to go too often. I do go, though, about twice a month for a couple of days or so. You can come with me each time. I have an apartment there.'

She nodded her head. He had mentioned the

apartment and she felt she would enjoy staying in the capital, in what she surmised would be a very luxurious apartment—if this magnificent villa was anything to go by. After a moment she asked him if he had any brothers or sisters.

'I've a brother four years younger than I—he's twenty-five,' he added so as to let her know his own age. She looked at him and thought he seemed rather older than twenty-nine . . . and yet she was glad he wasn't. . . . A circumstance that puzzled her until she realised she didn't want him to be a great deal older than she.

'Where does your brother live?' she inquired, breaking the silence that had fallen.

'In Athens; he's married with a small son.'

'So we shall probably see him and his family?'

'Not this first time, if you're not feeling up to it.'

'It's just that—that . . .' She toyed with her croissant. 'I don't like people knowing—er—thinking that I'm your—that you and I . . .'

'Perhaps they won't,' was his slow and cryptic rejoinder, and Melanie's eyes flew to his.

"What do you mean?'

'Perhaps I shan't have you for my pillow-friend after all.' He frowned at the expression and Melanie's puzzlement increased.

'I still don't understand, Vidas?' There was an edge of complaint to her tone which seemed to amuse him greatly, for his eyes glimmered and a half-smile curved the fine line of his mouth. How handsome he was! And how bronzed. The snow-white shirt was just the thing to accentuate a skin the colour of teak.

'What would you say if I were to ask you to marry me?'

'If—!' She stared, eyes dilating, the room beginning to revolve around her. 'What did you say?'

'I believe you heard.' He seemed impatient with her surprise, and a little bored as well, for he lifted a hand to suppress a yawn.

'I can't believe I heard right,' she gasped. "You—you asked me to—to marry you!'

He was shaking his head.

'Correction: I asked what you would say if I were to propose marriage to you.'

She swallowed to rid her mouth of excess moisture.

'It's the same thing,' she almost snapped, wishing she could think straight.

'Not quite.' Vidas reached for the coffee pot with maddening calm and asked if she wanted a fill up.

'I need something stronger than coffee!' she could not help retorting. 'Just what are you about? You certainly weren't serious—'

'Another correction: I have never been more serious in my life.' He poured her some coffee and then filled up his own cup. His eyes glimmered again, because she had said she needed something stronger than coffee, and because she was sitting there, bolt upright in the chair, stiff and still as a statue, staring at him across the table with an expression of accusation not unmingled with bewilderment. He was actually laughing at her and for one wild moment of near uncontrol she could have thrown something at him! Instead she said, marvelling at the steadiness of her voice,

'If you are serious, then perhaps you will give me a reason?'

'You still haven't answered my question: what would you say if I asked you to marry me?'

'No, of course!'

'Why?' So cool again! Was the man slightly mad? she began to wonder.

'Because I don't know you—that's one reason, and the other is that you don't—I mean,' she corrected hastily, 'we don't love each other.'

His dark eyes were narrowed, subjecting her to a keen and all-absorbing scrutiny. Melanie held her breath. She knew of his keen perception and could only hope and pray that her slip hadn't provided him with a clue to her feelings for him! How humiliating if he should guess that in a few short hours his superlative masculine attraction had been effective enough to make her fall in love with him! And what of his already inflated ego? It was with heartfelt relief that she heard him say, after that long and probing look,

'In Greece marriages are often arranged and so there is no question of their being based on love.' He paused a moment. 'Marriage to me would undoubtedly be the best thing for you, Melanie, at this particular time in your life. You'd have my name, legally, and my protection, should anything happen.'

'Should I be traced, you mean?' she asked, for the moment diverted from the main issue.

'It's possible,' he warned.

'But you assured me I'd be safe in Greece, on your island,' she reminded him, and now it was her turn to watch closely, hoping to read something from his expression, but it was impossible. 'It was because you gave me that assurance that I agreed to come and be your—your . . .' She trailed off to silence with pink rising in her cheeks. He gave a quirk of laughter but his humour was only momentary. His tone was serious when he spoke.

'I expect you would be safe enough here,' he conceded. But then he added at once, 'I want to marry you, Melanie. I believe you realise that I'm serious because even though you've known me for so short a time you've already learned a lot about me.'

She was silent, studying his proposal even though she knew she wouldn't be able to give him an answer at this time—no, not until she had thought it over properly— Her musings jerked abruptly to a halt. What on earth was she thinking about even to be considering his proposal! Marriage . . . to a man who did not love her! A man who was a self-confessed rake. And added to this was the fact that he believed her to be a thief.

She heard herself say, slowly and with a certain catch in her voice, result of the love she felt for him,

'I can't marry you, Vidas,' and then she added, recalling his avoidance of an answer before, 'There must be a reason why you want to marry me.'

He hesitated for a space and then he answered her.

'There are several reasons, not least of which is that it's time I settled down and raised a family.'

'But that's not the main reason?'

'No,' he admitted readily, 'it isn't. The main reason is that I want to convince Delia once and for all that there's no chance at all of my marrying her.'

So forthright! Melanie had not expected him to lower his pride to that extent. She was greatly puzzled by so many things, but yet within her mind was the certainty that, if she could cherish one spark of hope that he would one day fall in love with her, she'd not hesitate to marry him, and become the mother of the family he mentioned. No greater joy could she conceive than to have his children . . . if they were conceived in love and not lust.

'She's done something to you, in the past?' ventured Melanie, spurred by his expression, which was relaxed, without even the flexed line to his jaw or the hard light in his eyes.

'She and her father,' he answered, and his eyes did glitter then, with anger and something akin to actual hatred.

'But you are not intending to tell me what it was?'

He looked at her for a long unsmiling moment.

'You are quite right, Melanie,' he replied at length. 'I am not intending to tell you what it was.'

But it transpired that Melanie was very soon to learn what it was. After breakfast she was approached in the garden by Stella who smiled and said eagerly,

'You said, Miss Melanie, that you would like to see my baby today!'

'Yes, of course.' She hadn't forgotten as she strolled in the lovely grounds of the villa, but her mind was occupied with what had taken place at breakfast time. Vidas had not pushed her for an immediate answer and she had promised to think over his proposal and give him an answer in a few days' time. One part of her mind, the commonsense part, urged her to give him a negative reply, but the other part, ruled by her heart, was showing her wonderful pictures of a handsome husband who loved her and was, therefore, ever faithful, pictures which included children, handsome and dark like their father, running about, playing on the lawns or the beach—that beautiful private crescent with its smooth golden sand. . . . Pictures created by fantasy, unreal and impossible, but oddly persistent.

'You come to the back garden and I show you!'

The little girl was sitting in a pram, her tiny fingers playing with some brightly-coloured beads which were suspended from the hood, which was up as protection against the sun.

'She's lovely!' exclaimed Melanie, bending to touch the hand. The child looked at her and gurgled, the big brown eyes sparkling within their frame of incredibly long, curling lashes. 'Oh, Stella, you are a lucky girl to have a daughter like this!' Something had stirred within Melanie; she had never had anything to do with children before, since none of her friends had started a family yet. In any case, most of them weren't even married.

'Lucky?' The girl seemed to glow all at once. *Efkharisto poli*—thank you very much!' She gave Melanie a lovely smile. 'Many people say that I not lucky to haf baby and not married. You see, men not want in Greece to marry girls who not good—you understand what I mean?'

'Yes, Stella, I do understand,' returned Melanie in gentle tones. 'But you are lucky—I think so anyway.'

'You wish you haf baby like my Theodora—*ochi?*'

'Yes—er—does *ochi* mean yes?'

'It mean no. *Ne* is yes in Greek language.'

'I see. Yes, I would like to have a baby like your little daughter.' An emptiness seemed to be affecting her as she stood smiling down at the child, so contented, so pretty with its dark curly hair and those enormous eyes.

If she married Vidas then she would in all probability mother a child like Theodora. . . .

'I glad you come here to live, Miss Melanie.' Stella bent to straighten the cover and Melanie noticed that although it was spotlessly clean it was by no means new, and she felt sure it had been passed on several times before it came to Stella.

'Are you?' Melanie's tone was still gentle.

'Yes, and I haf hopes that you stay long time. I didn't like that other one whose father was so bad to Mr. Vidas!'

After a long pause, during which she debated on whether or not to pursue this subject, Melanie was hearing herself say,

'Miss Oliver's father did something bad to Mr. Vidas. What was it?'

'He get Mr. Vidas's father very much of the drunk and then gamble with the cards—you understand?' Melanie nodded and she went on, 'Mr. Vidas father gamble part of this island, which all of its has been in the family for many years. Mr. Vidas he very black angry but nothing he can do. Mr. Oliver he want Miss Delia to marries Mr. Vidas and he say he then gives back the land.'

Melanie was silent, digesting this. She spoke at

length, to ask what part of the island it was which was lost in the gambling.

'It the very best part! The Castro is there—only the walls, you know, preserved. Is that the right word?'

'Preserved, yes. Do go on, Stella.'

'It a Venetian castle—in Greece there are manys castles from these long away days. The lion of Venice ees over the door of the Castro and it ees very beautiful. There is some of the beach, too, that Mr. Oliver haf! And at the back of this beach is the Temple of Apollo with big columns and it is nice here to picnic, but not now that Mr. Oliver owns it. He not let anyone walk on it if he know, not even Mr. Vidas. So always Mr. Vidas want this land back and we all think he would marry Miss Oliver—' She stopped a moment and then continued, 'I like it if you stay and be Mr. Vidas pillow-friend. . . .' She trailed off and coloured beneath the darkness of her skin. 'Not mention this word because it not nice, but you know what I mean?' She smiled in such a disarming way that Melanie found herself saying quietly,

'I understand, Stella, but I am not Mr. Vidas's pillow-friend.' Not yet, she added, but silently.

'Oh, then I sorry! I thinks that if you haf come here with him it will be nice for you to— I like you to stay anyway, please, Miss Melanie!'

'I shall certainly stay for a while,' she promised and heard the girl give a satisfied sigh.

'Then Mr. Vidas not marry that one!'

'But if he doesn't he'll never get the land back,' Melanie had to point out.

'I thinks that if Miss Delia believe he haf another woman then she leave this islands and then she will sell this land to Mr. Vidas!'

'It belongs, at present, to her father.'

'He die in one—two—weeks—!' Stella shrugged her shoulders. 'He haf very bad heart attacks and is in the hospital. My cousin is nurse there and she tell me that he dies in one—two—weeks!'

'I see. . . .' Melanie's voice trailed as she saw Vidas striding through the *perivoli* towards where she and Stella were standing by the pram.

'I'm just taking a look at Stella's baby,' said Melanie before he could speak. 'She's a darling!'

He looked down at her with a strange expression.

'You seem to be fond of children,' he observed, still staring into Melanie's eyes.

'I've never had anything to do with them, unfortunately. But now—oh, I shall certainly take an interest in this adorable baby!'

He smiled enigmatically and told her he wanted to speak to her in his study. She said goodbye to Stella, patted the baby's hand and then followed swiftly to catch up with Vidas.

'Is it something important?' she asked, curiosity getting the better of her. He made no answer until they were in the study.

'Yes, it's important. I want you to marry me, Melanie, even though it might not be permanent—'

'Not permanent?' she broke in swiftly, unaware of the colour leaving her face. 'But—but I was under the impression that Greeks don't believe in divorce.'

'You're right, they don't. But one has to be influenced by circumstances and in our case it would

be rather in the nature of a business arrangement.'
He stopped as she began to shake her head.

'I'm not interested,' she said briefly and would
have left the study but he was at the door before she
was able to get there.

'You'll marry me, but only if it's permanent?'
Something unfathomable in his voice and manner
arrested her attention.

'You'd prefer it to be permanent?' she said curiously, and he nodded at once in response.

'I would, because as I have earlier said, I want to
have children. But I asked you about a temporary
marriage in the belief that *you* might not want it to
be permanent.'

She fell silent, trying vainly to set her mind into
some sort of order whereby she was able to marshall
clear-headed, far-sighted thoughts that would lead
her to a wise decision. She was at present influenced
by two things: her love for Vidas and the fear that,
should she refuse to marry him, he would then
marry Delia even though he obviously disliked her.
She could fully understand his wish to get back his
land, land which had been lost to him through the
perfidy of Delia's father. She could not be quite sure
that he would marry Delia, but she felt convinced
that, if he did, he would very soon be revenged on
her by taking up his old way of life; he'd be
unfaithful to her until, in the end, she would probably divorce him, but of course he would already have
made sure she had handed over the land, either
through purchase or gift.

'Can't you make up your mind, Melanie?' she
heard him say and looked up, biting her lip.

'No,' she sighed, 'I can't. In any case, what reason is there for this new urgency?'

'Mr. Oliver is dying,' he answered slowly, telling her what she already knew. 'He has only a few days to live at the most. Delia will then own the land—my land!' he added harshly. 'If I am married it's my belief that she will leave Thristos, and if she does, and is forced to find herself a home, she'll have no alternative than to sell me the land, since her father has precious little else to leave her and as she's never worked she can't maintain herself unless she raises money on that land.'

'It's all very logical thinking on your part.' Melanie spoke her thoughts aloud, recalling Stella's words and that others had come to the same conclusions as Vidas about Delia's leaving the island.

'For your part,' Vidas said, 'marriage will ensure your safety and also it will give you security for life.'

She shook her head, not a negative gesture but one of doubt and uncertainty.

'I did promise to think about it,' she said at last. Her big eyes were limpid and pleading as she added, a catch in her voice, 'Please leave me to think it out for myself.'

'Very well.' His voice sounded brusque, she thought, but then felt she might be mistaken, since there was a half-smile on his lips and his eyes had a softened quality about them. 'I shall be here, in my study, for the rest of the morning, but I'll join you for lunch.'

'Yes. . . .' She moved and he opened the door for her. Their eyes met as she passed him and for a second she shut hers tightly. If only she could harbour one atom of hope. . . . But no, a man like

Vidas would never fall in love with anyone like her— Melanie's thoughts cut as she remembered his saying she was the most desirable woman he had ever made love to.

Could physical desire ever progress to love? With children to help it was surely possible. . . .

Chapter Seven

To Melanie's surprise Vidas never came to her room that night, nor the next or the one after that.

She surmised that he was waiting to see if she would marry him before. . . . His control amazed her for doubtless she was as physically attractive to him as ever and his one and only reason for helping her was to make her his mistress, since at that time he had no notion of marrying her. It was the illness of Mr. Oliver which had instigated Vidas's wish to marry her in haste.

Vidas was busy in his study in the mornings and on one occasion he was there for the whole of the afternoon too. Melanie missed his company and would wander in the grounds or go and sit on the beach. Once she had been in for a swim but she was restless, unable to reach a decision, and with the problem hanging over her it seemed quite impossible for her to concentrate on anything at all. She made a point of seeing Stella's baby at least once a day, and one morning she wheeled the pram down to the waterfront where she sat in the open at the *cafeneion* and had coffee while watching Theodora playing in her pram. She was just beginning to toddle, but as yet Melanie had not ventured to take her out of the pram. On another occasion when she was playing with the child she became aware of Vidas watching her from an upstairs window of the villa and she did wonder if he were hoping this interest in someone else's baby would be what in the end would make up her mind for her. He would have guessed that she would like a child of her own and this in turn would give him a certain amount of confidence regarding her acceptance of his proposal of marriage.

It was when she had been at the villa for six days that the feeling of restlessness began to affect her in several other ways. Not only was it that a galaxy of doubts continually assailed her about the idea of marriage, but she was more and more anxious to know what was going on at home. Dared she phone Katie? was a question repeated many times a day. How were her parents? Was her father still safe in his job or had he been given notice? Soon, her parents would be expecting a letter from her because she had always written regularly between visits. Another question cropping up incessantly was: could Vidas eventually fall in love with her if she married him, or would there never be any attachment stronger and deeper than the physical one?

At last—and perhaps helped by the fact that Vidas was on a brief visit to Athens, going there and back in the day—Melanie decided to risk everything and phone her sister. She was through swifter than she expected and it so happened that Katie answered the phone.

'Melanie!' The gasp from the other end came over clearly, as did the vehement, 'Are you mad, ringing me at the office!'

Melanie's mouth tightened, but she managed to answer without any show of temper.

'You don't seem anxious about me, Katie—'

'Of course I'm anxious, but this is crazy! Supposing Mr. Meyer's listening?'

'I'm risking it,' snapped Melanie, now feeling quite reckless. 'Aren't you curious to know where I am and how I am getting on?'

A sigh of what sounded like exasperation came over the line.

Melanie made an angry face.

'Well, where are you and how are you getting along?' It was plain that Katie would be far more comfortable when Melanie terminated the call.

'I'm in Greece—'

'What!' Real interest now and no thought of ringing off—which had been Katie's intention though Melanie did not know it. 'Are you joking, or speaking the truth?'

Quickly Melanie explained, interrupted now and then by small, disbelieving exclamations from the other end.

'It's incredible!' gasped Katie when her sister had finished. 'Are you going to marry the man?'

Ignoring that, Melanie then asked what had happened.

'The police know it was you who stole the money—'

'They *think* it was I!' corrected Melanie, scarcely recognizing the harshness of her own voice.

'Okay, but does it matter? It's all blown over as far as this office is concerned. The police are looking for you but you know what they are these days—like everyone else, half-hearted where their job is concerned. I guess they'll write the case off in no time at all.'

So unconcerned! For the first time in her life Melanie actually felt dislike, and disgust, for her adoptive sister.

'Father?' she said, still keeping the anger from her voice. 'He paid the money back, I suppose?'

'Of course, and guess what? They've decided to keep him on. I was amazed because I didn't like that boss of his at all.'

'And you,' murmured Melanie, her tone now bitter. 'You and Hal . . . ?'

'We're fixing the date for our wedding very soon. Sorry you won't be here to be bridesmaid—'

'So everyone is happy?' broke in Melanie, echoing words spoken that first evening by Vidas. 'All except me.'

Silence. Was Katie at last feeling a pang of guilt?

'What did you tell the police?' demanded Melanie when the silence became long and strained.

'I had no alternative than to say you'd run off with the money and that I didn't know where you were. How did you get to Greece without your passport?'

'It happened to be in my handbag.'

'How fortunate—seems like fate. What's this guy like? Good-looking? Rich? A lot of Greeks are rich—'

'I'll give you my address,' broke in Melanie curtly,

'and I want you to send on some things—my private papers for one thing, my Birth Certificate—they're all in one envelope in a suitcase on top of my wardrobe.'

'You're mad at me, I can tell.' A pause and then, 'I can understand, in a way, but after all my parents and I have done for you, Melanie, it's not much to pay back. You've prevented a great deal of unhappiness, and in my opinion prolonged Father's life—and perhaps Mother's too, for don't think she'd have lasted long if Father had died, especially if he'd died in jail.'

'You can cut out the pathos!' snapped Melanie, now at the end of her patience. 'I'll write letters to Mother as usual, send them on to you, and you in turn can see that she gets them. I'm giving you my address now, and then I'll ring off.'

'But—this man—' began Katie, but her sister interrupted her with a curt,

'Here is my address.' She voiced it slowly, spelling out the name of the island. She then said a brief 'Goodbye' and rang off.

She was trembling as she stood by the phone and her eyes were filled with tears. It seemed impossible that Katie could be so cold and callous after the friendship that had existed between them. Perhaps, though, it was real fear, successfully hidden, that had made Katie speak as she had. For she must surely sometimes wonder if the truth would ever come out.

The one thing that seemed to have been of profit as far as Melanie was concerned was that, in some quite inexplicable way, the conversation with her sister had brought a certain peace to Melanie's mind.

She was no longer in doubt about her answer to Vidas's proposal of marriage. It would be yes.

The package which Melanie had asked for arrived within a week. Vidas accepted it from the postman and so Melanie was glad she had confessed to having phoned her sister. He seemed to doubt the wisdom of it but said very little. He was pleased at Melanie's acceptance of his proposal and the wedding date had been fixed as soon as Melanie received her package.

She and Vidas were married in Athens, with his brother and his wife being the only guests. Phivos was a serious young man with black curly hair and a teak-dark skin like his elder brother. His wife was petite and pretty, with long dark hair and big brown eyes. Her name was Artemis, and the little boy's was Davos. He was three years old, bright and happy, and he and Melanie were soon getting along so well that Phivos laughingly said,

'You had better take that rascal home, Melanie!' And, not sparing the new bride's blushes he added with a sly glance at Vidas, and in the customary outspoken Greek way, 'You and Melanie had best be quick to make a baby! Or this girl will be stealing one from its pram!'

Laughter all around with even Melanie able to join in; she felt lighthearted, able to crush any doubts that might now and then enter her mind. She had made her decision and that was that, she thought philosophically.

Both Phivos and Artemis had shown curiosity at

being introduced to Melanie on her first visit to the capital with Vidas. It was understandable, of course, seeing that there had been no intimation that Vidas was even interested in anyone.

'Love at first sight!' exclaimed Artemis who was plainly a romantic. 'Vidas, you must have taken heed of my reprimand that you were not looking for a wife.' She spoke excellent English, as did her husband, and even the child could make himself understood. Accents were there, though, rather more emphasised than that of Vidas who, Melanie had learned, spent several weeks a year in England.

Artemis when she managed to get Melanie alone wanted the 'full story,' but having been briefed by the man who was then her fiancé, Melanie told Artemis that she and Vidas had met at the house of his friends in England, become attracted to one another and had decided to get married.

'But why didn't you marry at home?' was Artemis's logical inquiry. Again Melanie repeated what Vidas had told her to, for with his keen perception he had anticipated all the questions his inquisitive sister-in-law was likely to ask.

'I wanted to see Thristos first, just to make sure I would like to live there.'

'But your parents? Aren't they upset that you're not being married over there? Shall they be coming here for the wedding?'

It had been a little difficult for Melanie to say she had no parents even though Vidas had pointed out that this was in effect true.

'Oh, sad!' from Artemis, who went on to put several more questions which Melanie was quite able to answer. The visit was brief in any case, and the next time they all met was at the Greek Orthodox church on a little hill overlooking the Acropolis of Athens. The sun was shining down from a sapphire sky and for Melanie this seemed to augur well for the future . . . hers and that of her very new husband.

Melanie would have liked to have a honeymoon but Vidas made no reference to one and she supposed that, under the circumstances, he felt a honeymoon would be something of a farce. How little he knew!

All Vidas's servants were delighted about the wedding but disappointed that it wasn't to be on Thristos, so that they could attend. Vidas promised them a party later.

After the ceremony which was in the morning the four lunched at the Grande Bretagne Hotel in Athens and then Phivos and his wife left them, having to hurry home because the nanny in charge of little Davos had previously asked for time off in the afternoon to visit her mother who was in hospital, having been in an accident the week before.

Melanie had a letter to post, telling Katie she was married, and this she did when she and Vidas were in the Plaka, the oldest part of Athens with its narrow streets, some like alleys, with a hodge-podge of medieval houses which had once been rather splendid but were now turned into *tavernas* and *cafeneions* where men sprawled on wooden chairs at pavement tables and played *tavli* with such deep concentration that they might have been gambling for thousands of drachmae. Other men watched, brown hands twirling worry beads or holding the

133

inevitable cigarette, while others were inside some of the cafes dancing to the strains of *bouzouki* music. It was all exciting and novel to Melanie and she often surprised a quirk of amusement on her husband's face when she exclaimed about something. He seemed happy, in a mellow mood, indulgent. She once asked him if he were bored.

'You must have seen it all many times before,' she added.

'There's always something new in the Plaka,' was all he said but she knew he was not bored.

'Can we go into one of these cafes?' she was asking as the afternoon wore on. Vidas had booked a dinner at an hotel, she knew, but that was not to be until eight o'clock and in any case, the cafes drew her, especially the ones where men were dancing.

'Of course,' agreed Vidas and took her to the Elatos, which was three storeys high with an open roof from where they had a panoramic view of the city with the Acropolis and its temples dominating the sundrenched scene. Vidas ordered *ouzo* for himself and Melanie asked for a long drink. Iced lemonade was brought by a white-coated waiter whose smile revealed several gold fillings. A woman came up to the table holding a tray of gardenias and jasmine. Vidas hesitated a moment and then brought forth some money from his pocket. The pretty posy was handed to him and he held it out to his wife. With a swift smile she accepted it and put it beside her glass. The gesture gave her inexpressible pleasure but she was guarded all the same, not wishing that Vidas should guess at her feelings for him.

A *bouzouki* band was playing and soon after Vidas and Melanie had sat down four young men began to swing and dip and twist their supple bodies as they danced through the *Zorba syrtaki*. When they had finished more men came, this time joined by knotted handkerchiefs, and performed a much more solemn dance: the *tsamiko*. Then these same men began another dance—rocking and dipping with incredible agility. Then one of them lowered his body to the floor and began twisting about and lifting his groin in what was umistakably an abandonment of erotic movements, and Melanie felt the colour sweep up into her cheeks. She heard a low laugh escape her husband, heard his whisper in her ear,

'All Greek dances—or almost all—are to do with Dionysian rites—ancient rites. Sexual gestures and other movements invariably are part of the dances that Greek men do.'

'You dance?' she asked, still feeling hot and embarrassed as the man continued his rotating, sexual movements.

'I do, yes.' Again he laughed. 'Don't worry, I shall not be giving you an embarrassing display like this.'

Tourists were enjoying the performance, Melanie noticed, and managed to compose herself again.

The Acropolis was the next place Vidas took her to and she was soon confessing that this place was one she had always wanted to visit.

'It's magic!' she was soon exclaiming, for undoubtedly the atmosphere of ancient Greece hovered immovably over the entire site.

'The Parthenon was a temple to Athena,' explained Vidas, clearly wanting her to enjoy this visit to the sacred hill of Athens. 'And Parthenon means: Virgin,' he added as they climbed the weathered, ancient steps. The sheer wonder of it all widened Melanie's eyes over and over again, and not least of the beauty was that of another kind—the view from the sacred hill over the city of Athens. A lot to mar it, like in any other great city, but there was magic in the view for all that.

The sun was sinking in the sky when at length they were at Vidas's apartment where they had stayed the previous night. A bath and change of clothing and they were off again to the Hotel Astir, where they dined in a rooftop restaurant, with all around them the magnificent view of the city. Vidas pointed out the great rock of Mt. Lycabettus, clothed partly with gracious pine trees; and facing them was the impressive sweep of the Acropolis with the Parthenon and Erechtheum illuminated in colour, as was the delightful little Temple of Nike. Lights everywhere, millions of them in every colour and combination of colours, twinkling, glowing, shimmering . . . all combining to form a polychromatic tapestry of breathtaking design. The air, too, was romantic, scent-laden and warm. For Melanie there was no sense of time, no conscious awareness of any problems or doubts, no fear of the future, and so no regret for the step she had taken in marrying this dark foreigner who, a mere few weeks ago was a stranger to her. Fate had sent her to him in the most improbable circumstances, and she now felt they were inextricably linked to one another . . . for the rest of their lives.

He said softly, looking at her in the pure light atmosphere around them,

'You're very quiet, Melanie. Where are your thoughts?'

She smiled and her eyes were limpid and wide.

'It's magical . . . that's what I am thinking.' She was telling a lie, but only a white one, she excused herself.

'We must come here again.' His tone was low but clear, with that attractive accent which supplied a certain fine timbre to his voice.

'I'd like to, Vidas.' She smiled again. 'Shall we be coming to Athens often?'

'Fairly. You will soon get to know your way around.'

'I'm sure I shall love this city just as much as I love London.'

He nodded and she wondered if he was thinking the same as she: would she ever see London again? He had often to go to England, he had told her, and in the ordinary way she would have gone with him, but for the present she dared not step foot on her homeland for fear of arrest.

'Come,' her husband was saying presently. 'It's time we were moving.'

Melanie stood before the elegant bird's eye maple dressing-table and stared at herself in the mirror, her lashes throwing delectable shadows on to her cheeks.

She swung around as her husband came almost noiselessly into the room, and automatically her eyes rested fleetingly on the king-size bed with its beautifully embroidered spread in white and blue and green. Vidas had a woman who looked after the apartment and she had obviously been told to have this room ready, for Melanie knew that when Vidas was alone he used another, smaller room which had in it more severe furniture, and a single bed.

As he came to her she saw at once that he was naked beneath the blue and gold dressing gown he wore. The cord was knotted lightly. His dark basalt eyes slowly travelled from her lovely face, a little flushed now, to her throat and the delicate slope of her shoulders, then lower still to the outline of her breasts and the tiny, darker buds that already seemed to be erect. The nightgown was transparent; she had bought it when on that first visit to Athens, and she knew it was sexy, seductive, knew that it would conceal nothing from the all-seeing eyes which even now were resting on a lower, darker place, and stripping the scanty covering from her altogether.

Her lips parted as if she would smile, but closed again. Her husband came forward to take the hairbrush from her fingers and place it down on the glass top of the dressing-table. She caught the scent of body talc mingling with the faintest hint of his maleness. She swallowed, unable to move as he stood close, his body almost touching hers. And then she was drawn into his arms, her lips possessed, her slender frame pressed close so that she felt the warmth of him . . . and the virility. Moistly his mouth caressed hers before seeking hypersensitive places behind her ears, the curve of throat and shoulders. With his hard chin he deftly slid away the narrow strap and then he moved away in order to lower the garment from her body altogether. It swirled about her bare feet and she was without cover, there for his eyes to linger on while his mind could have been ineffectually telling him to be patient. For Melanie, already a fierce longing spiralled through her, but yet she was all confusion when with slow deliberation he removed his brocade robe and laid it on the dressing-stool.

'Come to me,' he ordered softly and she obeyed, sliding her strong young arms upwards over his chest to let her fingers curl into his hair after caressing his nape. He was crushing her to him, his hard demanding mouth moist and mobile, enticing and persuasive. Melanie had the heady sensation of spinning, weightless, into a realm of gentle rapture and vaguely she was conscious of his expertise in moving without undue haste. Yet she rather suspected that he was impatient, that his longing was as great as hers. His warm flesh was ecstasy against her, and strangely she was not embarrassed by his very obvious need of her and the fulfilment she could give him.

'Melanie. . . .' His voice was hoarse, throaty, vibrant with passion. 'What is it that makes you so different from all . . .' His voice trailed as Melanie stiffened in his arms. She was hurt and she freed herself to turn away. Her lips formed the words he hadn't said,

'. . . all the others.'

He gave a small, rather impatient sigh.

'Melanie, you know very well that I've had others.'

She nodded, mouth quivering. She now had her back to him and she suddenly felt his hands cupping her breasts, felt her body being pulled against his.

Why was she feeling like this? It was stupid and she had no excuse for herself. Vidas was a self-confessed rake, a womaniser who had no regrets for the life he had led. He would have raped her, probably, on that first evening if she had fought him—and of course if there hadn't been any interruptions. Yes, he was just about as bad as any man could be, morally, and she had known it when she consented to marry him. She heard herself say quietly,

'I'm sorry.'

He made no response; in any case his mouth, avid and moist, was sensuously exploring the curve of one shoulder and then the next, while his masterful fingers closed on her nipples, to imprison them ruthlessly until they rose to hard, erect little buds of desire. Heat rose in wave after wave to suffuse her whole being; she squirmed and writhed, held in the inescapable grip of primordial passion, her back against his hard frame, his manhood pressed into her soft and pliant curves. He turned her presently and for a long moment their eyes were locked, his glittering with fire unquenched, hers dark and dreamy as a sensation of delicious languor mingled paradoxically with the fierce longing for the final ecstasy.

He seemed to smile, and bent to sweep her slender body into his arms. His flesh seemed softer now, like silk against her warmth. A few strides and he was at the bed, laying her on top of the cover, his hands caressing her stomach as he slowly brought them away. He went to switch off the light, leaving only the subtle and romantic glimmer of light from a tiny, rose-coloured bulb in the lamp beside the bed.

It suddenly came to Melanie that she was by no means the first woman whom he had made love to on this bed; the tiny light bulb was not there by accident, or because there didn't happen to be a larger one available. But she knew she had to forget whatever he had done in the past, or even what he might do in the future. Tonight he was hers alone, her husband, which none of the others had been, and with a little smile on her lips she waited for him to lie down beside her, to caress her soft skin, to dally again for a while, which he did with the finesse which only the fully experienced lover could display.

And then he was on top of her, a storm of passion bringing his manhood to her, and she steeled herself for the pain. But to her surprise he marshalled control at what was a crucial moment and so his love-making was gentle, so gentle that she scarcely had time to experience the pain before the pleasure overwhelmed it, wave after wave of rapture shaking their bodies as they became one, united and forgetful of all but the storm of ecstasy that increased in force until it seemed their bodies were being torn asunder.

The storm passed and the rapture dissolved into the delicious languor of afterplay. Vidas gently caressed her shoulder, her breast, her thighs. She in turn touched him gently, lovingly, with her hands, and her mouth that trembled against his chest where a small gold crucifix lay tangled in a nest of strong black hair.

'Good night, Melanie,' she heard him say in soft and sleepy tones, and he turned his back on her, but pulled her arm around him and held her small hand tightly in his.

She snuggled close and said,

'Good night . . . my husband. . . .' He was breathing evenly. She smiled and snuggled even closer. She gave a happy sigh and then she, too, was breathing evenly.

Chapter Eight

Melanie stared at the girl who had come sauntering up to her as Melanie came out of a shop. It was a week after the wedding and three days after the funeral of Delia's father.

There was no hint of sadness about the girl . . . but there was a look of sheer hatred in her eyes that sent a little quiver along Melanie's spine; she felt as if an icy cold finger was feathering its way along it.

'I've been wanting to speak to you privately,' she heard Delia rasp. 'Perhaps we can go over there and sit with a cup of coffee?'

Melanie frowned her objection, but within seconds curiosity was getting the better of her. She glanced at the *cafeneion* which was the typical outdoor cafe with the tables and chairs spilling out on to the sunlit pavement. Hibiscus bushes and oleanders adorned the walls of the building, and its background was the low hills where nestled a village of white and blue houses with the gleaming white campanile of the church rising above, silhouetted against a cloudless, sapphire sky.

'All right,' she agreed and began to move at the same time as Delia. A stocky waiter came at once to show them a table.

'Two coffees,' ordered Delia before Melanie could speak. Her voice was sharp, her chin thrust out. She glanced balefully at Melanie, impatient for the man to go from the table.

'I suppose,' she said grittingly, 'that you are congratulating yourself on your catch?' Harshness in the tone, but in the dark eyes something Melanie felt she should have noticed before, as she felt sure it had been there when Delia met her in the street. Triumph . . . ? How could it be? There was more reason for defeat than triumph, decided Melanie, and yet that look was certainly there.

'I hadn't ever thought of Vidas as a catch,' she retorted crisply. 'You're not at all delicate in your choice of words, Miss Oliver.'

The dark eyes glittered and for a moment there was silence. Melanie frowned, angry that she should be experiencing this tinge of apprehension.

'I've been over to England,' she said slowly but with fine emphasis, her eyes never leaving Melanie's face which, at the girl's words, had lost a little of its colour.

'You have?' She tried to sound unconcerned but the apprehension had increased.

'I know who you are.'

Melanie gave a start and her eyes dilated. Her

mouth felt dry and it was some time before she could speak. And when she did all she could find to say was,

'You do?'

Delia laughed, a harsh, grating laugh which attracted the immediate attention of the two sprawling at the next table, playing *tavli*. They turned their heads, looked from one girl to the other and then went back to their game.

'A criminal, a thief wanted by the police. Wait till Vidas knows!'

'He already does—' Melanie broke off, wishing she hadn't said that, wishing she had waited until she had spoken to her husband. However, what was done was done and Delia was staring at her with a look of suspicion.

'I don't believe you,' she said slowly, her eyes never leaving Melanie's face.

'Don't, then.' Perhaps it was this which, oddly, convinced the other girl that what Melanie had said was in fact the truth.

'He knew before he married you that you're a criminal?' Melanie said nothing and after a frowning moment Delia went on, 'What did you want the money for, anyway?'

'That,' retorted Melanie in glacial tones, 'is my affair!'

Delia shrugged her shoulders.

'I give you that point, it isn't, nor am I really interested. What interests me,' she went on with a heavy frown, 'is why Vidas married you knowing about the theft. There's some mystery. . . .' Her voice trailed and her eyes narrowed to mere slits.

'I've got it!! He did it to spite me! He figured out that if he was married to someone else I'd be forced to sell him the land! I never would have thought he'd go that far, though. It's unbelievable! But it proves the marriage is one of convenience on both sides and it won't last in consequence!' She fell silent for a few seconds of frowning concentration. 'You were on the run when you met him, weren't you?' she asked, eyes bright now as she congratulated herself on working it out. 'Yes, on the run, and he was wanting a wife! How very fortunate for both of you. I knew he was in England—' She stopped on a note of impatience as if she considered this bit to be a waste of time. 'How did you meet?'

'Again that is none of your business!'

'Well, at all events you were fleeing from the police. He offered to help in return for your cooperation. It isn't difficult to put the bits of the jigsaw together.'

Melanie heard herself say, looking at the girl with a curious expression,

'Do you mind telling me how you came by your knowledge?'

'That you were a thief? It did have an element of luck about it,' she murmured reflectively and almost as if she were speaking to herself. 'You see, when Vidas introduced you I felt sure I'd seen you before somewhere. The name "Grayshott" bothered me. I knew it was the name of a small town in Surrey but I also felt I'd heard it somewhere else. And it came to me when Father, regaining consciousness just before he died, asked me to let his friend in England know—if Father should die, that was, which undoubtedly he knew was to be the case. That friend, by some coincidence, happened to be a Mr. Meyer—'

'Meyer!'

'That's right.' Delia was thoroughly enjoying herself now. 'Father and I had visited Mr. Meyer in his office about three years ago and you came in with a message from your boss. You didn't look at me but of course I looked at you. I also heard him call you Miss Grayshott, but the name was lost to me until Father mentioned his friend.' She paused, but Melanie said nothing and she continued, 'I sensed a mystery when I knew Vidas had brought you here, and so instead of writing to Mr. Meyer I decided to go over. I had a good excuse for calling, and after I'd told him about Father's death I casually talked of the last time I was there, with Father. But I couldn't think of a way to mention that a young woman had come in while we were there. But as luck would have it your sister came in; she's Mr. Meyer's secretary—'

'My sister—?'

'Oh, I didn't know this young woman was your sister, not at that particular time. But when Mr. Meyer said "Thank you, Miss Grayshott," I naturally pricked up my ears.'

'Naturally,' agreed Melanie, quite unable to hold back the word of sarcasm in spite of how she was feeling.

'It was then a simple matter to manoeuvre the conversation, mentioning another Miss Grayshott who'd come in on my previous visit, and it was then that he said you no longer worked for him. I knew that, of course, since you were here. However, I asked why you had left and it was then that he told me you'd stolen eight thousand pounds from the wages bag.'

'Mr. Meyer ought to have kept it to himself!'

'Feeling injured!' exclaimed Delia. 'Well, if that doesn't beat all! He's the injured party, having all that stolen from him.' Melanie said nothing; she was ready to go, wanted to be alone so she could think. 'I shall of course tell Vidas, even though you say he already knows. I want him to learn that *I* know.'

'I can't think that it would trouble him unduly,' Melanie said with a touch of bravado. She was of the opinion that Vidas certainly would be troubled that Delia knew his wife was wanted by the English police.

'I shall also have to decide how else I can use the information I have,' mused Delia with a faraway look in her eyes. 'I'm sure I shall think of something.'

Melanie's eyes raked her with contempt.

'What kind of a woman are you,' she demanded, 'to stoop to a trick like that? To plan it all and go over to England especially to pry into someone else's private life? Aren't you thoroughly ashamed of yourself?'

A harsh laugh escaped the other girl, a laugh without humour.

'Vidas was mine!' she rasped through tightened lips. Her face had coloured with a greyish hue which made her appear almost ugly. 'And he'll still be mine because he never meant his marriage to you to be permanent! He's never ever contemplated marriage —except to me!'

'I don't believe he would have married you—'

'He would! To get the land. He still will, when he realises that his scheme has misfired and that I'm not intending to sell out to him! Why, I'd rather sell out to someone else, and unless he comes to see reason I shall!'

'Do you really want to marry a man who doesn't love you?'

'You did,' was Delia's swiftly-spoken riposte and for this Melanie had no answer.

Vidas was frowning heavily by the time his wife had finished what she was saying. For the time being she left out the fact that Delia had threatened to sell her land to someone else unless Vidas agreed to divorce Melanie and marry her.

'I'd never have believed that even Delia could be so malicious as that,' he frowned.

'She was puzzled by your bringing me here, which was understandable, Vidas, you must admit that.'

'And so?' with that arrogant lift of his brows that was somehow a part of his make-up.

'She would be suspicious as well.'

'About what?' Another lift of his brows and then, 'My actions are none of her business and she should know it by now.'

'Yes, but—' Melanie broke off as Nico came to the patio where they were sitting. He carried a coffee tray which he placed on the rattan table.

'Shall I pour it, Mr. Vidas?'

'No, Nico, we'll manage, thank you.'

'Delia had hoped to marry you,' said Melanie when he had gone. 'As far as she knew you weren't ever interested in anyone else.' She paused a moment then said guardedly, 'Do you feel confident, Vidas, that she'll sell the land to you eventually?'

'Completely confident; she has no option, having no assets but that land. Her father's dead and she will have to return to England and set herself up in a home, which she can't do without money.'

Melanie was troubled. She felt she ought to tell Vidas that Delia might sell the land to someone else, but she was at the same time most reluctant to give him anxiety. She thought it a shame that Vidas should be forced to pay money for the land anyway, seeing that it was rightfully his in the first place. She thought of his father's folly in gambling away part of his land—not just ordinary land, but an actual part of his island home. She found herself saying reflectively,

'You told me your father was a very good-living man. One would, therefore, expect him to be wise as well.'

The ghost of a smile curved her husband's lips.

'The two don't always go together, Melanie. On that particular occasion Father had had too much to drink, though why I shall never understand because he wasn't a man to indulge in that way.'

'It was most unfortunate.' Melanie's voice was regretful and sad and her husband shot her a swift, unfathomable glance.

'I agree,' he said, leaning forward to take up the coffee she had poured for him—thick black Turkish coffee which didn't suit Melanie's palate at all, and so she was drinking Nescafe with cream.

'Do you suppose Delia will try to get even with

you—I mean, will she carry out her threat to find a way of using the information she has?'

'We can only wait and see.' His mouth shaped itself into a thin and ruthless line. 'I'll talk to her if and when she comes to me with her information about your theft.' He seemed to stop somewhat abruptly and when Melanie looked at him she saw that his face had relaxed; the thin line of his mouth had dissolved into a smile that made her heart give a pleasant little leap. She responded, reflecting on her optimism and feeling sure it was not misplaced. For a week she had been deliriously happy, with Vidas kind and tolerant. On the occasion of her buying Stella's baby some clothes and a new pillow and covers for the pram, Vidas had seemed faintly amused and indulgent in spite of his saying on a little warning note,

'Squandering all your allowance? You only get paid once a month, remember.' She knew for sure that he was pleased she should be spending her money this way, giving herself pleasure and at the same time helping Stella.

And now . . . he was still smiling at her, his eyes plainly appreciative as they took in the clear glowing skin, the lovely eyes and the halo of shining hair. For her part, she was as always vitally aware of him as a man—the inordinate attraction of that chiselled leanness of the jaw, the firm and thoroughly masculine chin that spelled mastery, the eyes, which could register softness even while remaining shrewd and deeply observant.

'You know,' she was hearing him say, 'I have an idea there is more to that business of the theft than you've admitted.'

She gave a start, hoped he hadn't noticed and said swiftly, 'I told you everything, Vidas.'

'You're sure?'

'Yes,' she replied, managing to meet that penetrating gaze, 'I'm quite sure.'

'You stole eight thousand pounds?'

She nodded her head.

'For my parents' sake,' she answered huskily.

'And your sister's, and the man she hopes to marry.'

'That's right.'

'You seem to have been interested in this man.'

'I—er—liked him once,' she confessed in a low tone.

'And now?'

'It wouldn't have been any use, anyway, since he fell in love with Katie on sight.' She had averted her head and he put a forceful finger beneath her chin, compelling her to meet his eyes.

'And now. . . . That is what I asked you.'

'Now I don't feel anything for him,' she replied in the same quiet tone of voice.

'Let us forget all else for the moment,' he suggested unexpectedly. 'I'm going to take you to the island of Hydra to meet some friends of mine.'

'You are?' Melanie's eyes lit up and a lovely smile came to her lips. 'Now—today?'

'Today.' Reaching for his cup he took a drink of his coffee.

'Why have you made up your mind so suddenly?' she just had to ask.

'I'm at a loose end,' was his casual reply. 'I've finished all the paper work I had to do and as I feel like a break we'll take a sail over to Hydra. It's not far.'

'I know; I've been looking at the map.'

'You'll like the island. There isn't any traffic—'

'No traffic?' she blinked. 'You mean, no cars, or anything?'

'That's right. You either walk or ride a donkey.'

Another bright smile broke.

'It sounds fun,' she said.

He looked oddly at her then lowered his lashes as if he would keep his expression from her.

'We'll have a couple of days there,' he said. Then he added after a pause, 'We'll visit some other of the islands. Not this time, but later. The islands of Greece are among the most beautiful in the world.'

'This one's beautiful,' she said, watching the smooth, glistening sea being ruffled by a speedboat racing across her vision. 'Yesterday I went to see the part you don't own. I just looked down from a headland, of course; I didn't trespass.' Not a very tactful word, she realised at once on seeing her husband's mouth compress. However, he said nothing and for the next hour or so they were both busy in their rooms packing what they needed for the two days away on the island of Hydra.

Melanie was ready first and Stella brought her suitcase down to the hall.

'Is that a new gardener we have?' asked Melanie as she caught sight of a lean young man weeding one of the far borders. 'I've not seen him before.' Strange, she thought, that Vidas hadn't mentioned employing another gardener.

'He's Nico's son, home from Crete where he works.'

'He's on holiday?'

Stella smiled.

'Yes, that's right. He came one others times when he was on holidays.'

'And he comes here and works in the garden, for Mr. Vidas?'

'He like working in gardens. He stay here with Nico—in Nico's villa— You knows, down the roads.'

'Yes, I know where Nico lives.' It was a villa just along the lane owned by Vidas. Nico lived there alone as he had no wife—or perhaps it would be more correct, mused Melanie, still watching the young man, to say that Nico *slept* at the villa, since he was invariably working until after dinner. He seemed to thrive on work and Vidas had said he preferred to be at his employer's house than at his own.

Melanie asked Vidas about him once they were on the yacht.

Yannis and Pavlos were ready to sail, and they had also prepared a very appetising lunch which Vidas and Melanie ate in the saloon.

'Demetrios?' he said with a hint of amusement. 'Yes, he does like to spend his days in the garden. He's a strange young man,' went on Vidas reflectively. 'He seems never to have affairs, which is most unusual for a Greek,' ended Vidas with a laugh.

'How old is he?'

'I believe he's about twenty-five. Most of our men are married by then—unless they are forced to wait for dowries, that is.'

'Dowries?'

'The system survives in small islands like this. And

in many parts of the mainland, too. And if a girl doesn't have the required house and land then her betrothed has to wait.'

Melanie was frowning at him across the table, her knife and fork idle in her hands.

'How long? And where does this dowry come from?'

'The girl's father and brothers—if she happens to have brothers—all work in order to build a house. The land is usually theirs anyway, since most people own land. So they build the house in a lemon orchard or some other land. The house is often built in stages over a number of years, as the money comes along. Often dowry houses are begun when the girl is still a baby.'

'What a stupid, outdated and shortsighted idea!' she exclaimed. 'Why, if the father and brothers were very poor the house might never get finished!'

'That's so,' was her husband's casual rejoinder. 'Which means the man has to wait and wait—'

'He might meet someone else, though.'

Vidas shook his head.

'That rarely happens because here in Greece the engagement is as good as a marriage. There's a church ceremony; the girl dresses up and so does the young man and there's a party of sorts. Both take the engagement very seriously and, in fact, often the couple live together.'

Melanie's eyes widened.

'But—I thought Greeks were very much against that kind of thing.'

'In unmarrieds, yes. But as I said, the engagement

is the marriage in most cases.' He paused to take a roll from the silver basket. 'You are obviously thinking of Stella?'

'Yes, I am,' she nodded. 'Stella seems to be very sure she'll never find a husband because of what she has done.'

'In the ordinary way she wouldn't.'

'In the ordinary way? What do you mean?' Melanie was puzzled by the look on her husband's face. He said slowly,

'Demetrios has only been coming to do gardening for me since Stella came.'

'Stella—! You mean—he likes her?' How wonderful if that nice-looking man had fallen in love with her!

'He more than likes her. He intends to ask her to marry him.'

'He told you? Stella has no idea at all.'

'Because she lives with this sense of shame, she takes it for granted that Demetrios could not possibly have any *honourable* intentions. But she is aware of his interest nevertheless, and if you ask me she likes him a lot.'

'How do you know he's in love with her?'

'He told his father. Nico mentioned it to me; he seemed troubled, but when I'd explained that if Demetrios marries here, then takes his wife to Crete, he can say he's been married for some time but he'd left his wife on Thristos. It's rather fortunate that Demetrios is a reserved young man who never talks about himself. I don't think he'll have anything to worry about at all. In any event, I've managed to convince his father that a marriage can and will succeed. I believe Demetrios intends to seek out Stella's father and ask for his consent—though Stella, being now under my care, doesn't need her father's consent to marry.'

'So it's the happy ending for Stella. Oh, Vidas, I am so very glad!'

Chapter Nine

The lovely island of Hydra, uniquely picturesque with its houses appearing to be piled one on top of the other on the steep and sinuous little alleys running up and around the rocky slopes. Mansions had been built there long ago by sea captains and it was in one of these that the friends of Vidas lived—Pericles and Maria Phytalis, both aged thirty and both artists.

The couple were there on the waterfront, and after the introductions and the curious looks and questions the four climbed up the steep path to the mansion, a beautiful edifice with immaculate gardens on several levels. Truly it was a steep and rocky island and barren in parts. But there was a certain indescribable attraction which in these days brought the tourists flocking to its shores. And because of the influx the numerous artists who used to live in the island had departed. But as Maria and Pericles had complete privacy in their house surrounded on all sides by its own grounds, they had no desire to leave. Their paintings adorned the walls, and one, of the waterfront, was presented to Melanie and Vidas as a wedding present. Maria, more curious than her husband, began questioning them when Pericles, stockily built and handsome in a rugged sort of way, went off to supervise something one of his gardeners was doing by the fountain.

'Dear Maria,' sighed Vidas after answering only two questions, 'your woman's curiosity is more avid than ever!'

She laughed, revealing two gold fillings. She was slender and looked at least five years younger than her age. Her hair was lighter than usual, and Melanie rather thought that the auburn colour had come from a bottle but it was exceedingly attractive for all that. Her eyes were dark grey, her skin brown and clear. She was pretty, and she used her lovely slender hands to advantage, bringing notice to them in several subtle ways. Vidas plainly found her slightly amusing but he liked her enormously; that was very clear to see. The camaraderie between Vidas and his friends included Melanie with quite amazing speed and she felt happier than ever . . . she felt she belonged. The accents of both were only slight and for the most part only English was spoken. But now, when Vidas was chiding Maria in this faintly mocking way, she said something to him in Greek. His mouth went tight, his glance shooting towards his wife. When he answered it was in English.

'A lot of people took things for granted, Maria. Delia was never really my kind of woman.'

Maria coloured a little, aware that she should have not mentioned the girl.

'You see I am avidly curious,' she said with a brightness designed to make him forget what had gone before. 'Well, Vidas, as long as you are my intimate friend—'

'Maria, you and I have never been intimate.'

'You—!' She glared at him then laughed. 'Wicked man! Always twisting things around! Melanie, it is to be hoped you can reform this—this rake!'

'Stop giving me away,' said Vidas, lifting a hand to smother a yawn.

'I daresay Melanie has guessed what you are—I mean,' she hastily corrected, 'what you have been!' She paused, then went on when neither of them spoke, 'If you are my friend then I have a right to know what led up to this unexpected marriage.'

A sigh and a frown but then Vidas said resignedly,

'We met in England as I told you on the phone. It was love at first sight and so there really wasn't anything to dally for.' He stopped as Pericles came back into the room. 'I've already told you all this, Maria, so what more is there to say?'

'Oh, well, nothing I suppose. But no one ever expected you to spring anything like this on your friends—' She looked at Melanie and made a wry face. 'Sorry, Melanie! You must not take offence. You will get to know me by and by!'

The two days sped by and Vidas and Melanie were again on the yacht, sailing for home. And they had not been in the house more than a couple of hours when Stella, who had been out walking her baby, came to Melanie in the garden where she was sitting in a little arbour on her own, Vidas being in his study. Stella wore a rather worried expression and seemed almost furtive, the way she glanced around before taking an envelope from her pocket.

'Miss Delia say to give this to you when Mr. Vidas not there.' Stella was now embarrassed; she passed the envelope over swiftly, took the handle of the pram in her hands and turned to walk away.

'When did she give it to you?' Melanie's whole body had begun to tremble.

'Yesterday. I tell her you are away on the yacht— She seem—what you say—in very angry mood.'

'Thank you, Stella,' murmured Melanie and the girl went off. Melanie held the small white envelope as if it were hot. She felt like taking it to Vidas but decided against it. Delia had told Stella to give it to Melanie when Vidas wasn't there.

She opened it slowly.

'I have informed the English police of your whereabouts. Your only hope is to go into hiding. You haven't much time.'

Every vestige of colour drained from Melanie's face and the hand holding the paper trembled visibly. Not much time. . . . The letter had been delivered yesterday. . . . There wasn't much time.

What must she do? Her mind became a blank and she was crying.

She felt there was only one thing to do: telephone her sister in order to get some information. Fortunately Vidas was still in his study, and as there was a phone in her bedroom Melanie had no problems about getting through undisturbed. This time it was the operator who answered, and without giving her name Melanie asked for Miss Grayshott. She was through in seconds.

'Melanie!' The voice at the other end was high-pitched and agitated. 'Oh, I'm so glad you rang! Though I don't know what's to be done! You see, I've just had an urgent call from Mother—just a couple of minutes ago—to say that Father's had a fatal attack and although he's in hospital the doctor's given him only a few days to live! Mother said I had to go up at once . . . we both had to go up at once. . . .'

'Both?' Melanie stared at the receiver for a paralysed moment, her brain struggling desperately to begin working again. 'Mother th-thinks I'm still working at Meyer's, of—of course—'

'You know very well she does! So what am I to say when I arrive home alone!'

'You're going now, at this moment?' Melanie's brain was still not functioning properly; she hadn't forgotten the reason for this telephone call to her sister, which was to get hold of some information regarding the fact that the police in England now knew where she was. She was overwhelmed with problems!

'Naturally I'm going at once!' was her sister's impatient reply. 'I was just about to tell Mr. Meyer that I'd have to have some time off.'

Melanie was quite unable to answer, with her brain still fogged and battling to find some light, some solution to this problem. Her father was dying and she could not go to him. . . . But if she was going to be arrested anyway, why not go home? She shook off the idea, then it loomed large again, only to recede, and she shook her head in exasperation at her inability to find a clear-cut plan of action.

'Are you still there?' from the other end and she was able to say yes, she was still here, trying to think.

'I ought to come over,' she said when Katie interrupted her.

'Come over? And be arrested the moment you step from the plane?'

'I don't believe that every airport has been alerted,' was Melanie's somewhat acid rejoinder. 'After all, I'm only a minor criminal in comparison to what goes on these days. I think I must seriously consider coming over,' she ended and for a long moment there was silence on the air.

'It's risky. And suppose you do manage to get home without being caught, you're sure to be caught later, and what's that going to do to Mother?'

'I might as well tell you,' said Melanie through dry, stiffened lips, 'that the police know where I am; they have probably been in touch with the Greek police already and someone could even now be on their way to arrest me.'

'The police know!' gasped Katie disbelievingly. 'But how can they?'

'I can't go into that now,' impatiently from her sister. 'I'll explain it all when I see you.'

'Your husband—does he know you're likely to be arrested?'

'No.' Melanie wondered if she looked as pale as she felt. 'I shall leave him a note, then get the ferry to Piraeus and from the mainland hope to get a plane. It'll take time so you'll have to make some excuse for the delay.' Her brain—thank God—was as clear as it could be now. She knew exactly what she was intending to do. But Katie had other ideas, and the agitation was in her accents again as she said,

'You can't come over, Melanie! You'll be arrested *here!* And what is that going to do to Mother? She is suffering enough as it is—she sounded devastated on the phone just now. If you were to be arrested and jailed it would be the end for her! Don't come, Melanie,' she begged, and a look of contempt entered Melanie's eyes. Katie was thinking of no one but herself. For Katie strongly suspected that Melanie, when questioned by the police, would break down and admit the truth. Melanie herself feared this, too, but on the other hand, she could not let her father die without seeing her just once more.

'I'm leaving all else in the hands of fate,' Melanie said with emphasised decision. 'The future can take care of itself; for the present—well, I want to see Father and I also want to comfort Mother at this time—'

'Melanie, you can't!'

'I'm ringing off now, Katie, because there's a ferry leaving here in less than an hour. With luck I could be home either very late tonight or early tomorrow morning.'

'Melanie—you can't ignore what'll happen in the future—the very near future! Why, Mother will still be in the throes of grief when you are arrested. She'll die! And you will be to blame.'

Melanie paused in thought. What Katie said could

164

be right, yet it was plain that she was so agitated as to be on the borders of hysteria.

'I'll make up some good excuse for you not being here,' she heard Katie saying desperately. "I'll say you've been taken ill—'

'But you've just been speaking to Mother, and obviously didn't say anything about my being ill,' Melanie reminded her.

'Oh, that! I can say I was too shocked by her news. Leave it to me, Melanie. Promise you won't come!'

Again Melanie hesitated. Yet, even if she were arrested in Greece she would be tried in England, so her mother would be bound to learn the truth anyway.

'I'm coming,' she stated emphatically and hung up before Katie had the chance of saying anything else.

It didn't take her long to write the note, which she left in Vidas's bedroom where he would be sure to see it. If he came from his study before it was time to dress for dinner, and she wasn't about, he would take it that she was either out shopping or taking a long walk on the beach. Melanie's one urgent worry was that he would just happen to come from his study as she was leaving the villa with her small suitcase. But as luck would have it she managed to get away, and on arrival in Athens she caught a plane within two hours of having arrived at the airport.

Chapter Ten

Melanie looked down sadly at the pale tired face and her heart caught and then throbbed painfully against her ribcage. Never would she have thought to see such a dramatic change in her father in such a short space of time. But she did recall that blue colour on his lips, and the tiredness in his eyes. Obviously, at that time, there had been more than anxiety over his lapse that had contributed to his looks.

'I'm going to die very soon, Melanie,' he said in no more than a whisper.

'No, darling—'

A feeble hand lifted from the bed cover halted his daughter's words.

'I'm not sorry to be going. So much has happened recently. And in any case, my love, if I live I shall be unable to carry on normally; I shall be always having heart attacks.'

'Father, please don't talk like that.'

'I'm facing up to it, Melanie. One has to some-time, you know, dear, for none of us can live forever.'

'No, but lots of people live today with the aid of pills and other medicines. . . . ' Her voice trailed away to a despairing silence as she recalled the fact that the doctor had held out no hope at all. Her father was going to die and nothing could be done to save him, nothing whatsoever.

Melanie sighed, her eyes smarting with unshed tears. She wished her mother had insisted on keep-ing him at home, for she hated this place with its cold white tiles and chromium and clinical smells. White figures flitting noiselessly about did nothing to help. What a place in which to die!

'Melanie. . . .' The voice was low and husky and very weak. 'I said so much has happened recently—'

'Don't think about it, darling,' she broke in hasti-ly, taking it for granted that he was referring mainly to his lapse. But to her dismay she heard the feeble voice say, as her father's hand sought hers, a hand so cold that a shiver of dread passed along Melanie's spine,

'My dear, why do you suppose I wanted to speak to you alone—why I sent Katie and her mother away? It was because I want to thank you for what you did. . . . ' His voice failed him for a few mo-ments and Melanie caught her underlip fiercely between her teeth as she saw tears oozing from beneath the half-closed lids. 'I don't know exactly what happened, or how you are going on, my dear child, but I do know that it was you who stole to save me from disgrace—'

'Father,' broke in Melanie in deep distress, 'please don't talk about it. I can't think how you know but—'

'When I came to think about it, after repaying the money, I began to dwell on my employer's remark that it was a very strange coincidence that my daughter should have a win at this particular time. It was *too much* of a coincidence, I began to think, and in the end I made Katie meet me and I questioned her. . . .' Again he paused to gather strength. 'I told her that I'd contact the Premium Bond people and at that she broke down and told me that it was you who had produced the eight thousand pounds . . . you had taken it from the wages.' His pale eyes were sightless now, from the tears. 'I asked Katie what had happened since and she said you—you'd been on the run but were now in Greece, having been helped by a Greek who has since married you.' His voice failed even yet again. 'Child, are you happy? Tell me all about it, and how you managed to get here if the police are after you.'

'Darling,' she murmured soothingly, 'everything's all right. I'm very happily married—'

'How can you be? Married in such a hurry—why? What was it all about? Who is this man? Where is he now? I want to see your husband.'

'I had to come away without him, Father. But do rest your mind, love. We're very happy—you see, I— We fell in love on first sight so naturally we decided to marry. And he's wealthy so I have nothing, absolutely nothing to worry about.' She was speaking almost mechanically, wanting to reassure him while her mind was on what Katie had done: told her father that she, Melanie was the thief . . . and yet in all fairness what other course could Katie have taken?

'You are sure you're happy?'

'Very sure, Father.'

'And the police—do they still want you?'

The silence was fleeting before Melanie said,

'No, they don't want me now, because Vidas, my husband, repaid the money and—and Mr. Meyer wouldn't prosecute.'

A great weight seemed to have been lifted from the man lying there on the bed, his ashen face turned up to hers, his pale eyes seeing better now as Melanie had dried them tenderly with her handkerchief.

'So I needn't die with this on my mind. . . .' He was a long way off and as a glazed covering affected his eyes Melanie caught her breath and something akin to panic seized her. She thought he was actually breathing his last, but he rallied and a stiff little smile touched the parched and colourless mouth. 'You've been a good daughter to us, Melanie, and forgive us if we've now and then favoured Katie. We knew we'd done it and felt unhappy—'

'Father,' broke in Melanie in gentle tones, 'forget it. You've both been wonderful to me. Why, where would I have been without you—your love and care?'

He sought her hand again and held it in a cold weak clasp.

'I'm glad we had you, dear Melanie. You've given us a lot of happiness. And now . . . you're rewarded; you are happy in your marriage— I wish I could have met your husband, my dear. Is that not possible? Surely, if you ask him, he will come over and meet me?'

'It's . . . difficult, Father. . . .' She was frightened but hoped he wouldn't notice. Frightened that she would be arrested before he died, and that he would then wonder why she didn't continue to visit him. If she were arrested tonight . . .

'Why is it difficult, dear?'

'He's a—a very busy man—'

'You know, if you are as happy as you say you are, then why didn't your husband insist on coming over with you? He should never have let you come alone, Melanie.'

'He wanted to—to come,' she lied, 'but I assured him I'd be all right on my own.'

'Well, I want to see him.' Suddenly he seemed to be imbued with a new strength. 'Go from here now and phone him, or cable. Say his father-in-law's dying and wants to meet him.'

Melanie stood there biting her lip, her mind confused, as it had been confused so many times recently.

'Apart from anything else,' her father was saying, 'I want to thank him for repaying that money you took.' He gave a sudden, unexpected sigh. 'There's so much I don't know about this whole business. It seems just as much a coincidence that you should meet and marry a rich man who was willing to pay out eight thousand pounds to a man he had never met. . . .' The old man shook his head against the snow-white pillow. 'All very strange and baffling. . . .'

'Father, love,' interrupted Melanie in soft and

soothing tones, 'don't worry yourself with it. I'd hoped I had assured you everything was all right. Vidas saw that if he didn't pay I'd be in trouble so naturally he paid. He did it for me, love, not for a man he had never met—did it to save me from the consequences of my act.' How she managed to lie so efficiently and look her father straight in the eye she would never know but she did manage it. And to her relief his face cleared and a smile was forced to his lips.

A nurse came in and quietly said it was time to go. Melanie bent and kissed his forehead and when he pressed that she would ask her husband to come over she said yes, she would phone him right away.

Mrs. Grayshott had been dazed when Melanie arrived at the house, and now, twelve hours later, she was still dazed, and her eyes were red and swollen from weeping. She seemed only to want to dwell on the far past, when she and her husband were first married and had all their lives before them. She had not even commented on the fact that Melanie had arrived much later than Katie—in fact, Melanie felt she wouldn't have bothered much if Melanie hadn't arrived at all, for she scarcely knew what was going on around her, obsessed as she was with dwelling on the past and regretting that it was all so long ago.

'You shouldn't have come,' sighed Katie when at last they were alone, having persuaded their mother to go to bed with a sleeping pill. 'You can expect arrest anytime.'

'Well, I did say I was leaving it all to fate.' Somehow Melanie seemed to have been able to fall back on some reserve she never knew she had—or perhaps it was that inbuilt medicatrix which is in everyone, which had come to her aid. She had no regrets on what she had done even though, once having left the island of Thristos, she could not for a moment take her mind off Vidas, or try to imagine his reaction to a note which said briefly,

'Having to go home as Father is not expected to live. Will obviously be picked up by the police and unable to return.' And because she knew it would be a long long time before she saw him again—if she ever did see him again—she could not resist ending with, 'I love you, Melanie.'

And she had unintentionally left Delia's note on her dressing table. . . .

Once at the hospital all else went from her mind, but now she was again thinking of Vidas—could not thrust his image from her mental vision; it was there, hovering in the background of everything else she did or said. Vidas. . . . A lump in her throat and sadness in her heart; nerves quivering at memories of his love-making . . . would she ever know its beauty again?

'I still say you shouldn't have come.' Katie was moving restlessly about the sitting-room; the drapes were apart and the garden could be seen, flooded with moonlight.

'I'm glad I did.' A small pause then, 'Father thanked me for what I'd done.' She failed to keep the bitterness from her voice even though she was again telling herself that Katie had acted in the only way possible under the circumstances.

'He—!' Katie's face lost its colour. 'I didn't get a

chance to tell you what I'd done. Mother was with us all the time.'

'It doesn't matter.' Melanie's ears were constantly alert for the sound of a car which would tell her the police had come for her. She found herself wondering how anyone could embark on a life of crime. Their nerves must be made of iron. Hers would be in shreds soon and she was almost hoping that the police would come and it would all be over, once and for all. But no—not while her father was alive. After that . . . well, as she had said twice to her sister, she was leaving it all to fate.

'Father wanted to see my husband,' Melanie reflected. 'I promised to phone and ask him to come over.' She had already told Katie that their father thought Vidas had paid the money back and, therefore, Melanie was safe.

'If you hadn't come back none of this would be bothering us,' said Katie with impatience. 'Mother is going to collapse when the police come for you.'

'They might not come yet.'

'You're hoping?' Katie shot her a glance of perception. 'You think your luck might hold out?'

'It could. I managed to get into the country without any trouble and who knows, as you say, my luck might just hold.'

'Until when?'

Melanie shrugged her shoulders. Was she, like her mother, in the kind of daze that almost completely fogged her mind? Of a surity something strange was happening for she seemed to be so philosophic about the whole situation.

'If you phone Vidas do you suppose he'll come?'

Katie was still moving about in that restless way and Melanie wished she'd sit down.

'I rather think he might. . . .' From where did confident words like that come!

'You do?' curiously. Katie stopped her walking about and looked down at her sister, sitting there in a low chair, her face very pale but on it a sort of calm reserve and resignation. 'Why, then, don't you phone?'

Melanie shook her head.

'I don't want to—just in *case* he should refuse.'

'Or give you a trouncing? Greek men are noted for their mastery over their womenfolk. He'll not be pleased that you've left without consulting him first.'

'I agree,' with a deep sigh. Melanie glanced at the clock. 'I don't think the police will come tonight now,' she said.

'Can you go to bed, with that on your mind?'

'You're so casual about it, Katie! Anyone would think it really was I who had done the robbery!'

'I'm sorry,' muttered Katie. 'Like you, I'm out of my mind with worry.'

'I think I shall go to bed.' Melanie put up a hand to hide a yawn. 'It's been a long, long day.'

'And I don't suppose you slept last night?'

'I—' Melanie's voice cut; the sisters stared at one another, eyes dilating.

'The police. . . .' Melanie felt slightly hysterical as she thought: I'll be getting used to this; it's the third time. Or was it the fourth?

The bell. Katie and Melanie were unable to move.

'What can you tell Father?' began Melanie as, all strength leaving her, she felt tears clouding up at the backs of her eyes.

'There it goes again,' from Katie. 'I hope Mother took that tablet. If she did she won't wake until the morning.' She looked at her sister. 'You're so white. You look ill.'

'I feel it.' Melanie moved like a robot to the door of the sitting-room and passed through. 'I'll go and see them,' she said, thinking of her father and of Vidas and wondering what would be the length of her sentence.

Reaching the front door she stood for a moment, but the bell ringing again spurred her into action for she had no wish that her mother should be wakened. She called to Katie as she put her hand on the latch, 'You'd better begin concocting up a story to tell Mother and Father.'

'I'm giving myself up!'

'You're—*what!*' But by now Melanie had the door open, steeling herself to face the uniformed men—or perhaps they'd send only one, seeing that it was only a woman— *'Vidas!'*

She gaped at him, standing there with a glowering expression on his face. Roughly she was pushed aside and the door was slammed shut.

'Yes,' he gritted, 'Vidas! And some trouble you've put me to! What the devil do you mean by running off like that without a word?'

'I—you—were busy and—and I didn't want to—to disturb y-you. . . .' She stepped back strategically as he made to grab her wrist. She had a strong suspicion that he would very much like to shake her, and she felt weak enough already.

'If—if you so much as t-touch me,' she added absurdly, 'I'll scream.'

'Did I hear you say Vidas? Thank God!' Katie,

175

equally as white as her sister, had come from the sitting-room into the wide rectangular hall and was examining the man who was Melanie's husband. 'You're not the police after all.' She scarcely knew what she was saying but she did know she was sagging with relief.

'How did you get here—?' Melanie stopped, flushing at the absurdity of these words too.

'I swam,' with heavy sarcasm. 'How else could I have managed to get here so quickly?' Vidas looked from Melanie to her sister. 'You were obviously expecting the police?'

'They'll be here any minute,' quaked Katie then added swiftly, 'No, we agreed that they won't come so late as this.'

'But you thought they were here now.'

'Yes,' they said in unison.

Vidas's dark eyes were narrowed as they looked from one to the other.

'Well,' he drawled at length, 'aren't you going to ask me in?'

'Of course.' Melanie could scarcely think as she moved automatically back into the room from which she had just emerged. 'Vidas, you shouldn't have come,' she began when he stopped her with a peremptory lift of the hand. Katie, who had followed him, now turned and seemed to be mesmerised by him. She stared, examining the classical features, the shining jet black hair, the proud head set on broad, square shoulders. Her eyes wandered to the sinewed, athletic frame, and she passed a tongue over her lips. She had always considered Hal to be the most handsome and masculine man she had

ever met ... but now. ... Her glance strayed to
the white face of her sister and she said, framing the
words slowly,

'I meant it, Melanie, just now when I said I was
giving myself up. I stole the money, not you, and so I
shall take the punishment.'

Silence, and the sort of atmosphere that could be
cut with a knife. And then Melanie was shaking her
head.

'You can't, Katie, for what about Mother—and
Father, too. No, leave it as it is—'

'I must,' broke in Katie in a distressed voice. 'Oh,
I know I've seemed to be very casual over the whole
business but within me there's been a battle raging
all the time. Why should you take the blame? In any
case, it will be a relief to confess and get this guilt off
my mind.'

'You'll go to jail! No, Katie, you said yourself that
Mother would die if she found out it was you—'

'Might I interrupt,' said Vidas with a sort of
smooth urbanity. 'First of all, no one is going to
jail—'

'Yes they are,' interrupted his wife. 'I mean, I am!'
She pulled up rather abruptly beneath the dark
censure of her husband's eyes.

'Melanie,' he said in a very soft voice, 'I'm
speaking. I expect you to listen to me without
interrupting.'

She coloured painfully, while Katie made a wry
face and wondered if Hal would be as masterful as
this once they were married.

'I think,' said Katie, 'that I'll introduce myself to
my new brother-in-law. Vidas, I'm Katie.'

It was just what was needed at this tense moment and all three smiled amusedly. Melanie just had to say, risking another reprimand,

'Aren't you very angry, Vidas?'

'I should have thought that was made more clear when I came in. Yes, I am angry, but,' he murmured cryptically and with an unfathomable expression in his deep-set basalt eyes, 'I shall deal with you when we get home.'

Again she coloured and made no more attempts to speak. She moved over to the window and looked out into the darkness while she listened to her husband saying again,

'As I have just remarked, no one is going to jail. The money will be paid back to Mr. Meyer first thing in the morning—'

'Mr. Meyer!' It was Katie who interrupted this time, she who received a look of censure from her brother-in-law. 'You've seen him? But how . . . ?' She trailed away to silence and again made a wry face. Melanie had wheeled around on hearing the words about the money being paid back to Mr. Meyer.

'How did I get to know about him? Firstly, Melanie had told me about him, and I got his address and home number from—' He looked at his wife now, '—Delia.' And his mouth was so tight, and his eyes glittering, that Melanie shivered, very sure that Delia had come in for a bad time at his hands. 'And if you are wondering how I got this address, it was from an envelope I found of yours, Melanie.' Vidas paused, then went on,

'I've phoned him,' with a glance at his wife. 'He's agreed not to prosecute.'

'How strange,' murmured Melanie with a faraway look. 'Father was so concerned about my being prosecuted that I lied to him, telling him . . . ' She looked at her husband and gave him a lovely smile. 'I told Father that my husband had repaid the stolen money and Mr. Meyer was not intending to take the matter any further.'

Vidas looked coolly at her and said, in that finely timbred voice she had come to love,

'You must have had second sight, my dear.'

'Vidas—' Katie took a couple of steps towards him. 'Thank you. I was determined to give myself up. Even as it is, I intend to let my colleagues at work know that it wasn't Melanie who took the money, but me.'

'No,' argued Melanie in a firm voice. 'There would be nothing to be gained. Don't you agree, Vidas?' She smiled at him, and as she saw his expression change her heart turned a somersault. He might be angry, as he asserted, and intending to 'deal with her' when they were home, but that look. . . . She couldn't be mistaken! Tenderness was there, even though a hint of mocking satire mingled with it. . . . Tenderness . . . and love? Of course, he knew that *she* loved *him*, since she had given it to him in black and white.

'Agree,' he said with raised eyebrows. 'I agree with Katie.'

'Katie?' with a bewildered stare. 'But—'

'You and I, dear, shall be visiting this country regularly and I have no wish that my wife shall ever be pointed at. Katie has the right idea, and if I am not mistaken she would insist anyway.' He turned to her. 'Am I right, Katie?'

She nodded her head.

'I've been rotten to Melanie and I intend to make amends. I'm very lucky that I'm not to be prosecuted, and that's all due to you, Vidas. Mother will never know it was I who stole the money—she doesn't know any money has been stolen, in fact. Father knows, though.'

Melanie looked distressed.

'Personally I can't see why you have to confess, Katie—'

'Melanie, dear,' broke in Vidas with a hint of asperity, 'the matter is settled. Forget it.'

She averted her head, wondering what Katie was thinking of Vidas's rather domineering manner.

'Melanie was saying, just before you came, Vidas, that Father wants to see his son-in-law before— before . . .'

'I shall see him in the morning,' promised Vidas and it was only then that both girls jerked their heads to look at one another.

Their mother had been completely forgotten for the past few minutes.

'Something wrong?' inquired Vidas with a look of puzzlement.

'When Father said he wanted to see you he— Oh, dear! What are we going to do!' Melanie quickly explained the whole situation to Vidas, mentioning every single incident since the moment when Katie had told her about the theft of the money. Both Katie and Vidas listened intently, Katie biting her lip and plainly using her brain in an attempt to think of some way out of this new problem, and Vidas likewise sitting there in silent, frowning concentration.

'So your father knows you're married but your mother doesn't?'

Both girls nodded as Vidas said this.

'When Father said he wanted to see my husband he didn't take into account the whole situation, but of course he's not really in full possession of his senses, and in any case, he was becoming very tired by this time.'

'Didn't your mother ask any questions when you arrived so much later than your sister?' he asked.

'Katie had previously told Mother I wasn't well and might not be able to come.'

'I didn't really think she would come, even though, on the phone, she said definitely that she would,' inserted Katie.

'Your mother's at the hospital now, I presume?'

'No, she's in bed, having taken a sleeping pill.'

'A fortunate circumstance,' mused Vidas, still frowning in thought. 'Had she been here when I arrived the situation would have been even more tricky than it is now. At least we have time to think of some way out of this mess.' He paused a moment. 'Your father knows your mother is in ignorance of the marriage, so it seems that the best way of solving the problem might be for you to say, Melanie, that I couldn't get to the hospital.' It was plain that this was, for him, not the ideal solution, since he realised that the old man ought to meet his son-in-law before he died if that were at all possible. 'You could in any case explain to him the difficulties involved, since his wife was not only in ignorance of the marriage but also of the fact that Melanie was supposed to have stolen from her employer.'

Both girls gave a small sigh.

'I wish there was another way,' said Melanie. She became thoughtful. 'Mother will have to know sometime that I'm married, so supposing I tell her now—in the morning, I mean?'

'She'll think it very odd your springing it on her,' pointed out Katie logically.

'I know—and I can't think how I would go about it. . . .' Her voice trailed away and she caught her breath. The sitting-room door had been left partly open and Mrs. Grayshott was standing there, a vacant expression on her face.

'Mother!' Both girls spoke at once. 'How long— have you been there?' added Melanie with a frantic glance at her husband.

Mrs. Grayshott shook her head from side to side, very slowly, her eyes still vacant. She was just staring and the three soon realised that she was scarcely aware of any of them.

'How long . . . ?' A frown of bewilderment creased her brow. 'I can't sleep,' she complained, like a child, fractiously. 'I want to go to my husband . . . he's calling for me . . . I keep hearing him—' She swayed and would have fallen if Vidas's speed and quick thinking hadn't taken him across the room in a flash.

'She needs a doctor,' he said crisply. 'Melanie, phone for one right away!' He was almost carrying Mrs. Grayshott to the sofa, with Katie moving towards them and Melanie running into the hall to telephone the doctor.

The old man on the bed looked up into the grave face of his son-in-law and managed a stiff little smile.

'I like you,' he murmured, his thin cold hand still gently clasped in that of Vidas from the introduction just made by his adopted daughter. 'I somehow knew you'd come—and so quick it was, but air travel is so efficient these days.' He stopped and withdrew his hand. It lay on the bed cover, blue-veined and with the knuckle bones white beneath the skin. 'Be good to my girl,' he murmured weakly. He looked at Katie and then around the small private ward he was in. 'Mary . . . where is she?'

Melanie swallowed and Katie turned away, neither able to tell him that his wife was dead, herself having had a stroke and dying in the early hours of the morning. It was Vidas who answered the question.

'She wasn't very well and so we advised her not to come today. I'm sure you understand?'

The old man nodded his head.

'She must have had a bit of a shock when she knew you were married, Melanie. . . .' His voice was fading; it was plain that he was becoming vague about what he was saying. 'My darling Mary. . . . Losing me and now you. . . . She's ill, you say?' A frown creased his forehead. 'But my Mary is never ill—'

'I'm afraid you must all leave now.' The white figure in her starched uniform, faintly formidable and yet there was compassion in the dark grey eyes. 'You can come back this afternoon.'

'Thank you.' Vidas again for neither girl could manage to speak.

'Goodbye,' they heard their father say after they had both kissed him. 'Goodbye . . . give your mother my love.'

They had been back at the house less than an hour when the telephone rang. The girls looked at one another because each had guessed it was the hospital.

'I'll answer it,' said Vidas and went from the room leaving the girls with tears in their eyes.

It was a week later and Vidas and Melanie were on the patio, both quiet as they drank their after dinner coffee. The sun had gone down in a blaze of multi-coloured glory and now the sickle of a young moon hovered like a hammock in a pale mauve sky waiting for darkness. It came swiftly and a million stars blinked through the deep purple of a Grecian night.

'Darling,' came Vidas's voice at last, 'don't be too sad. They went together and were buried together. You know it's what they'd have wanted could they have planned it themselves.'

She nodded in agreement.

'I know you're right,' she said, but with a catch in her voice, and tears too. 'Mother wouldn't have wanted to live once Father had gone.' She thought of the way her mother had always leant on her husband, of the many times she had shown that she would never be able to manage on her own. More than once she had said she would want to die if ever she were widowed.

'Neither suffered the pain of missing the other,' Vidas was saying gently. 'I'm sure you'll agree that when two people love as deeply as that there can be little left to live for when one of them dies.' So grave the tone . . . and carrying a quiet significance which could not possibly be mistaken.

And suddenly Melanie's burden of grief seemed to fall from her and a lovely smile broke. Vidas rose from his chair, moved to hers and pulled her gently to her feet.

'My love,' he murmured close to her cheek, 'I'm glad I could help to dissolve that sadness, take that haunted look from your eyes. It's been there for a week and it was making me sad, too. Oh, I know you will be some time getting over a loss like that, but try always to be glad they went together. Promise me.'

'I promise.' She lifted her face, inviting his kiss. He had not made love to her since the funeral four days ago. He seemed to know she did not want him, not then. But now . . . His dark observant gaze looked into her heart and his mouth curved in a smile of profound tenderness.

'The note you left,' he murmured after kissing her with tender passion, 'told me what I'd already suspected.'

'That I love you,' she returned simply.

'Did you guess that *I* loved *you?*' Tilting her face with a masterful hand beneath her chin he kissed her softly parted lips again.

'You were kind to me, and I began to hope that you would come to love me.'

'I couldn't resist you—' He broke off to kiss her again, this time with increasing passion, and his hands slid down from her tiny waist to her thighs and stayed there. She clung to him, caressing his nape, nuzzling her face against his ear so that the lobe was caught between her lips. She knew an access of triumph and pleasure as a little tremor passed through him, causing his hard frame to quiver against her. 'It wasn't just physical, my darling,' he continued after a long while. 'You mustn't ever think that. And, my dearest, you know, don't you, that you have nothing to fear? My "bachelor days" are past—and now I'm a very settled married man who has the most beautiful wife in the world.' Vibrant the tone, and more noticeably accented because of the ardour that edged it. 'My love, I said I'd done a good night's work when I shielded you from the police, and nothing was more true.' He held her from him, looking at her in the starlight, the breeze from the sea ruffling her hair. 'I began to suspect there was more to that business of the robbery and I was right. You lied to me more than once over that,' he reminded her censurously.

'I wanted to make a confession, Vidas, but it seemed logical to me that you'd believe I was trying to put the blame on my sister just to gain your regard.' She paused then added, 'It was hard for me to bear the thought that you believed me to be a criminal.'

'I don't think I ever regarded you in that particular light,' he reflected. 'After all, it was in a good cause,' he added with a touch of amusement.

'Katie acted on impulse,' returned Melanie. 'And as things have turned out it's resulted in nothing but good.'

'Because you and I would never have met.'

How strange was fate, she thought.

'I haven't thanked you for paying Mr. Meyer back the money,' she said after a long interval from which she emerged breathless and aroused.

'There isn't any need—' Vidas broke off and frowned as Nico appeared at the french window behind them.

'The telephone, Mr. Vidas . . . er—Miss Oliver.'

'Thank you.'

It was less than three minutes before Vidas returned and there was a look of satisfaction on his face. He had previously told Melanie that he'd convinced Delia that he was in love with his wife and also that she would have a very thin chance of selling the land to an outsider.

'She's agreed to sell?' Melanie spoke before he could and he nodded instantly.

'I've had to pay a good deal more than I should but at least it's to be in the family again.'

'I'm so glad she was able to see reason in the end.'

'She'll leave within a month, she says.'

Again Melanie was glad, for she would not have liked an old flame of her husband's living so close. However, all she said was, thinking of Delia's note that had been left, and naturally read by Vidas,

'She wasn't able to do either of us any harm, after all, in spite of her threats.'

For a fleeting moment his mouth went tight, and Melanie did wonder what kind of a scene had been enacted when, after reading that note, Vidas had gone to see Delia at her home.

'No, she wasn't able to do either of us any harm,' agreed Vidas, taking his wife in his arms again and pulling her close. 'It's all in the past now,' he added then bent his dark head to lock his lips to hers, while his hand moved sensuously over the delicate slope of her shoulder, then down to let the lean brown fingers deal with three small diamanté buttons securing the neckline of the wild silk evening blouse she wore. His fingers slid into the bodice, filtered into the lacy bra to tease the sensitized little buds and cause his wife's eager body to curve and press until it seemed she was melded inextricably with his granite hard frame. The bra was pulled down and a breast was cupped, kneaded and possessed; the agony of longing quivered through Melanie's loins even before his other hand slid in almost arrogant possessiveness to her lower curves and began to squeeze and knead in the same provocative way.

'Vidas,' she moaned softly as she curled her fingers into his hair, 'I . . .' her voice trailed as heatwaves spread through every cell in her body. She felt heady with desire, weak beside his masculine strength; she knew the excitement of expectancy, the glory of his masterful hands taking their pleasure and giving it. She could see the volcanic fire in his eyes, feel the demanding roughness of his tongue on hers, knew a weakness in her limbs and moved her hands from his hair to rest on his shoulders. Her body was arched, compelled by his crushing strength to shape itself to his, while a wild, primitive longing sent searing flames of agonising heat into her loins.

'Vidas,' she moaned in desperate urgency, 'let's go in. . . .'

Sweeping her into his arms he strode to the french window, and through it, and if he saw Nico standing in the hall he chose to ignore his presence as he carried his wife up to their bedroom. Once there, he put her down; she flung her arms about his neck and murmured huskily,

'I love you, my dearest husband!'

He said nothing, but smiled and picked her up again. . . .

IT'S YOUR OWN SPECIAL TIME
Contemporary romances for today's women.
Each month, six very special love stories will be yours
from SILHOUETTE. Look for them wherever books are sold
or order now from the coupon below.

$1.50 each

☐ 5 Goforth	☐ 28 Hampson	☐ 54 Beckman	☐ 83 Halston
☐ 6 Stanford	☐ 29 Wildman	☐ 55 LaDame	☐ 84 Vitek
☐ 7 Lewis	☐ 30 Dixon	☐ 56 Trent	☐ 85 John
☐ 8 Beckman	☐ 32 Michaels	☐ 57 John	☐ 86 Adams
☐ 9 Wilson	☐ 33 Vitek	☐ 58 Stanford	☐ 87 Michaels
☐ 10 Caine	☐ 34 John	☐ 59 Vernon	☐ 88 Stanford
☐ 11 Vernon	☐ 35 Stanford	☐ 60 Hill	☐ 89 James
☐ 17 John	☐ 38 Browning	☐ 61 Michaels	☐ 90 Major
☐ 19 Thornton	☐ 39 Sinclair	☐ 62 Halston	☐ 92 McKay
☐ 20 Fulford	☐ 46 Stanford	☐ 63 Brent	☐ 93 Browning
☐ 22 Stephens	☐ 47 Vitek	☐ 71 Ripy	☐ 94 Hampson
☐ 23 Edwards	☐ 48 Wildman	☐ 73 Browning	☐ 95 Wisdom
☐ 24 Healy	☐ 49 Wisdom	☐ 76 Hardy	☐ 96 Beckman
☐ 25 Stanford	☐ 50 Scott	☐ 78 Oliver	☐ 97 Clay
☐ 26 Hastings	☐ 52 Hampson	☐ 81 Roberts	☐ 98 St. George
☐ 27 Hampson	☐ 53 Browning	☐ 82 Dailey	☐ 99 Camp

$1.75 each

☐ 100 Stanford	☐ 110 Trent	☐ 120 Carroll	☐ 130 Hardy
☐ 101 Hardy	☐ 111 South	☐ 121 Langan	☐ 131 Stanford
☐ 102 Hastings	☐ 112 Stanford	☐ 122 Scofield	☐ 132 Wisdom
☐ 103 Cork	☐ 113 Browning	☐ 123 Sinclair	☐ 133 Rowe
☐ 104 Vitek	☐ 114 Michaels	☐ 124 Beckman	☐ 134 Charles
☐ 105 Eden	☐ 115 John	☐ 125 Bright	☐ 135 Logan
☐ 106 Dailey	☐ 116 Lindley	☐ 126 St. George	☐ 136 Hampson
☐ 107 Bright	☐ 117 Scott	☐ 127 Roberts	☐ 137 Hunter
☐ 108 Hampson	☐ 118 Dailey	☐ 128 Hampson	☐ 138 Wilson
☐ 109 Vernon	☐ 119 Hampson	☐ 129 Converse	☐ 139 Vitek

Silhouette Romance

Coming next month from
Silhouette Romances

Sweet Second Love by Anne Hampson

For two years Linda Kendall believed her life was over—then she met handsome Duarte. However, she didn't want to fall in love again, it was too painful. But when she looked into Duarte's eyes she knew it was already too late.

Forbidden Affair by Patti Beckman

Jacquelyn's passionate romance with Scott had been shattered when she demanded the freedom to pursue her career as a designer. Now with her career in full bloom, could she yield to a love she once was denied?

Dance At Your Wedding by Josie King

When Jason tricked Linda into posing as his wife on a business trip to Madeira, Linda vowed he would never learn that he was the one man she wanted full-time and forever!

For Eric's Sake by Carolyn Thornton

Shaw agreed to help model Brandy Logan gain custody of her sister's child by marrying her—but only temporarily. Now Brandy found herself in love with a man who wanted out.

Ivory Innocence by Susan Stevens

Ivory vowed to use any weapon she could to avenge her grandfather. But upon meeting Matthew Kendrake she found herself caught between her own campaign of revenge . . . and love.

Western Man by Janet Dailey

For years Sharon Powell had idolized Ridge Halliday, the arrogant rancher whose Western Colorado spread adjoined her family's. Fortunately, she was now immune to his lazy sensuality and meaningless love games—or was she?